TOTAL HEALTH™

TALKING ABOUT LIFE'S CHANGES

TEACHER'S ANSWER KEY

SUSAN BOE

purposeful design® publications
Colorado Springs, Colorado

Purposeful Design Publications is the publishing division of the Association of Christian Schools International (ACSI) and is committed to the ministry of Christian school education, to enable Christian educators and schools worldwide to effectively prepare students for life. As the publisher of textbooks, trade books, and other educational resources within ACSI, Purposeful Design Publications strives to produce biblically sound materials that reflect Christian scholarship and stewardship and that address the identified needs of Christian schools around the world.

Printed in the United States of America
25 24 23 22 21 20 19 18 8 9 10 11 12 13 14 15

Boe, Susan
Total health: Talking about Life's Changes
Second edition
Total Health series
ISBN 978-1-58331-233-9 Teacher's Answer Key Catalog #7605

Purposeful Design Publications
A Division of ACSI
PO Box 65130 • Colorado Springs, CO 80962-5130
Customer Service: 800-367-0798 • www.acsi.org

Table of Contents
Student Workbook: Teacher's Answer Key

Name ______________________ Date ____________

Vocabulary (Teacher's Key)

Match the seven words below with the corresponding letter from the list at the bottom of the page.

Deception ___*E*___

Temptation ___*B*___

Consequences ___*D*___

Habits ___*A*___

Soul ___*G*___

Influences ___*C*___

Total Health ___*F*___

a. a repetitious pattern of behavior

b. an attraction to something, often harmful

c. the power to produce change through people or situations

d. the outcome or result

e. misleading deliberately

f. the all-encompassing well-being of a person

g. the mind, will and emotions

The Two Trees (Teacher's Key)

In the space provided, list the thoughts, actions, and attitudes that represent each tree.

- Dependent on God
- Needing others
- Involved
- Talking with safe adults
- Telling the truth
- Open and transparent

TREE OF LIFE

- Independent from God
- Not needing others
- Isolated
- Not talking with safe adults
- Covering up
- Closed and afraid

TREE OF DEATH

How can a person successfully win this daily conflict between these two trees?

"Me, Glorify God?" YES! (Teacher's Key)

BIBLE STUDY

1. Who is the greatest hero in your life?

   Who is your favorite actor or actress?

   When you get emotionally excited about your favorite hero or favorite star, tell others about them, and go to see their movies as much as you can, you're really "glorifying" them. Look up the words "*glory*" and "*glorify*" and in the dictionary. How do you think that these definitions apply to God?

   To "glory" means to "boast in" or "be proud of" someone or something. To "glorify means to treat someone as more splendid and excellent than others. In relationship to God, it means to praise, admire, and worship God. It also means to live in such a way that others will be drawn to serve and praise God, too.

2. Read *John* 16:14. When a person is born again, God sends His Holy Spirit to live inside of them. What does the Spirit do in and through Christians' lives? (It's something that increases more and more all the time throughout a Christian's entire life.)

   The Spirit glorifies Jesus Christ in greater and greater ways in and through us, just like He did in Christ's life.

3. Look up *Psalm* 50:23 and *Matthew* 5:16. In the first verse, in what two ways do we glorify God? In the second, in what way do we as Christians bring honor to God? Is verbally praising and thanking God enough to really be "glorifying" God?

   In the first verse, by praising Him verbally and by living right. We "walk the talk". In the second verse, by having non-christians observe our good works. No, verbal praise isn't enough. Our lives must also be lived in ways that will draw people to Jesus.

4. Jesus said, "By this My Father is glorified, that you bear much fruit..." (*John* 15:8) What do you think that He meant by "bear much fruit"? How does that bring praise to God?

   He meant to lead people to Christ and have those people become strong, stable Christians: "that your fruit might remain", (v.16).

(*cont.* ➻)

5. Do you think that Christians can glorify God even in the "negative" experiences of their lives? Read the following verses and list the two "negative" or painful experiences in which Christians can bring praise to God.

• *John* 21:19, Christians can glorify God in their...

deaths; when they die for Him. "By what death he [Peter] should glorify God..."

• *I Peter* 4:16, Christians do glorify God when they...

suffer as Christians; being persecuted for the gospel and/or for morality

6. Read *I Corinthians* 6:20. In what two areas of our lives does Paul say to "glorify" God? What do you think Paul means by glorifying God in these two areas of our lives?

"Glorify God in your body and in your spirit" means to obey what God's Word has to say about our physical, sexual, and spiritual areas of life and, thereby, bring Him praise.

7. When Jesus said, "And I do not seek My own glory..." (*John* 8:50), what do you think that He meant? How do you think that *Revelation* 18:7 would contrast with that?

Jesus humbled Himself and only did His Father's will. "Babylon, the Harlot" (the Roman empire of the first century; also all proud nations of the earth) seek their own greatness and power rather than God's. God judged her by the hordes of eastern army invasions. "In the measure that she glorified herself and lived luxuriously, in the same measure give her torment and sorrow, for she says in her heart, 'I sit as queen...'"

8. Read *Jeremiah* 9:23,24. In what three areas did the prophet say people should not be proud and arrogant? How do you think this applies to the American culture or to your life?

1.) "Wisdom " (education, knowledge, information, academic degrees).
2.) Political Power and military might.
3.) Money and wealth.
"Thus says the Lord: 'Let not the wise man glory in his wisdom. Let not the mighty man glory in his might. Nor let the rich man glory in his riches. But let him who glories glory in this: that he understands and knows Me; that I am the Lord, exercising lovingkindness, judgment, and righteousness in the earth. For in these I delight,' says the Lord."

(*cont.* ➻)

"Me, Glorify God?" YES! (Teacher's Key, cont.)

BIBLE STUDY

9. Concerning *Jeremiah* 9:23,24: in what four things does God delight (because they give Him glory)? Give one example of how each of these points applies to your life.

   1.) *Getting people to know and understand Him (salvation, sanctification).*

   Example:

   2.) *Showing lovingkindness (mercy) to people.*

   Example:

   3.) *Showing judgment upon evil.*

   Example:

   4.) *Showing righteousness to people (the faith-righteousness of the gospel as well as justice and morality).*

   Example:

10. God wants to glorify Himself through you! After doing this Bible study, in what areas of your life do you want to "glorify" God more?

God's Promises to Me (Teacher's Key)

"By which have been given to us exceedingly great and precious promises, that through these you may be partakers of the divine nature."
II Peter 1:4

Look up the following verses, then match the most appropriate promise with each verse. (There may be more than one verse for some promises.)

- K *James* 1:5
- C *Psalm* 147:3
- I *Philippians* 4:19
- F *Psalm* 141:3
- B *Jeremiah* 29:11
- D *Psalm* 51:2
- G *II Timothy* 1:7
- L *Psalm* 29:11
- M *Matthew* 11:28
- J *Psalm* 23:4
- E *I Corinthians* 10:13
- A *Psalm* 32:8
- G *Isaiah* 41:10
- H *Psalm* 147:5
- A, B *Proverbs* 3:6
- L *Philippians* 4:7
- G *Psalm* 27:1
- E *Romans* 8:37

A. God will direct and lead my life.

B. God will take care of my future.

C. God will heal my broken heart.

D. God will forgive my sins.

E. God will give me strength when I am tempted.

F. God will help me not to gossip.

G. God will help me when I am afraid.

H. God will comfort me when no one understands me.

I. God will take care of all of my needs.

J. God will comfort me when I am lonely.

K. God will give me wisdom when I ask.

L. God will give me peace when I am stressed-out.

M. God will help me when I am tired.

Name ____________________ Date __________

Vocabulary (Teacher's Key)

Match the circulatory related terms from the list below with the definitions and put the correct letter in the blank after each definition.

1. The component in the blood that fights germs, viruses and diseases __j__
2. The smallest blood vessels found in the body __d__
3. A disease which involves hardening of the arteries __a__
4. The component of the blood responsible for carrying oxygen __c__
5. A severe restriction of blood flow to part of the brain __g__
6. The portion of the blood that causes clotting __e__
7. The force placed against the inside walls of your blood vessels __f__
8. Blood vessels that carry oxygen-depleted blood back to the heart __i__
9. The liquid portion of the blood __b__
10. Blood vessels that carry oxygenated blood away from the heart __h__

a. arteriosclerosis
b. plasma
c. red blood cells
d. capillaries
e. platelets
f. blood pressure
g. stroke
h. arteries
i. veins
j. white blood cells

Part Two

Circle the correct answer of those given after each definition.

1. The ____ cleanse the blood of impurities and send it back to the bloodstream. (Pharynx, small intestine, (kidneys))
2. A balanced, stable environment within the body would be called ____. (stroke, hormones, (homeostasis))
3. The long muscular tube which includes many digestive functions and runs throughout the body is the ____. ((alimentary canal), esophagus, diaphragm)
4. The small flap of skin that prevents food from entering the trachea is the ____. (diaphragm, (epiglottis), pharynx)

(cont. ➻)

5. The process of breaking down food and making it usable for the body is called ____. (digestion, homeostasis, arteriosclerosis)
6. The portion of the digestive tract responsible for waste functions is the ____. (esophagus, small intestine, large intestine)
7. A passageway that carries air to the lungs is called the ____. (epiglottis, trachea, diaphragm)
8. The heart muscle could also be called the ____. (smooth muscle, skeletal muscle, cardiac muscle)
9. The basic building blocks of the body are called ____. (veins, cells, capillaries)
10. The ____ is often referred to as the throat. (pharynx, epiglottis, trachea)
11. The ____ release hormones when we are under certain types of stress. (kidneys, cells, adrenal glands)
12. Most digestion and absorption of nutrients takes place in the ____. (small intestine, large intestine, alimentary canal)
13. "Chemical messengers" released by the glands of the endocrine system. ____ (platelets, hormones, plasma)
14. If an individual is experiencing a state of physical, mental, social and spiritual well being that person can be said to be ____. (healthy, tissues, homeostasis)
15. Similar cells organized into specialized groups to carry out particular functions could be called ____. (platelets, hormones, tissues)
16. An ____ exists when two or more tissues are grouped together to perform a particular function. (alimentary canal, organ, ovaries)
17. The passageway responsible for carrying food to the stomach is the ____. (epiglottis, small intestine, esophagus)
18. The rate at which the body metabolizes food is controlled by hormones released from the ____. (testes, ovaries, thyroid gland)
19. The glands of the female reproductive system responsible for female sex characteristics are the ____. (testes, pituitary gland, ovaries)
20. Muscles found in the digestive system and blood vessels are referred to as ____.(cardiac muscles, platelets, smooth muscles)
21. The glands responsible for male sex characteristics are called the ____. (kidneys, testes, ovaries)
22. Human growth hormone is released by the ____. (testes, thyroid gland, pituitary gland)
23. The ____ are the principle organs of the respiratory system. (lungs, kidneys, adrenal glands)
24. Muscles responsible for the movements of the body are the ____. (smooth muscles, cardiac muscles, skeletal muscles)
25. The chest and abdomen are separated by a muscle wall called the ____. (epiglottis, diaphragm, trachea)

The Life of a Cell (Teacher's Key)

Color the picture of the cell and list the eight common characteristics of every cell. What is meant by the phrase, "Good health begins at the cellular level"? How might this phrase relate to poor health as well?

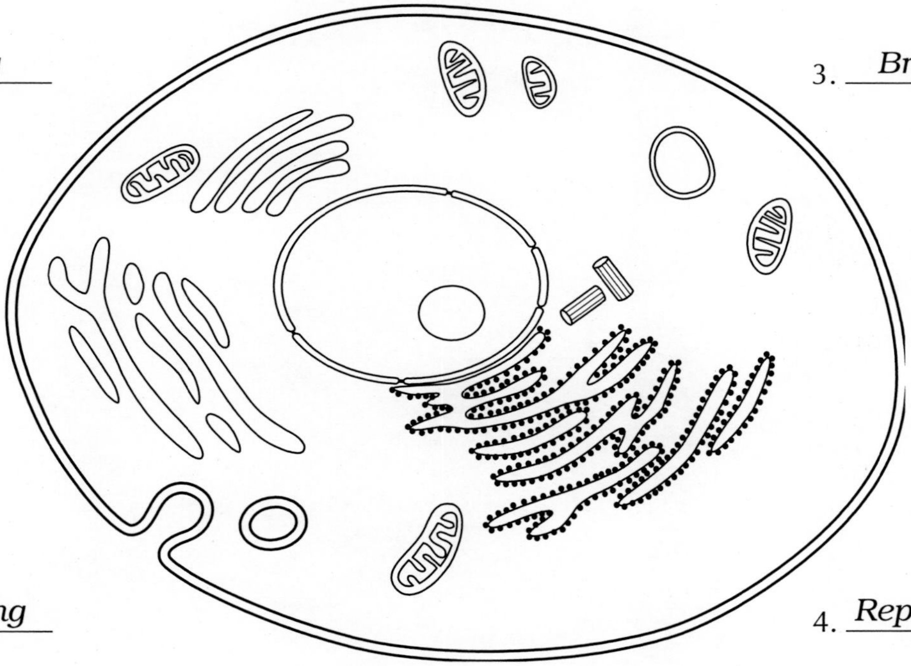

1. *Moving*
2. *Sensing*
3. *Breathing*
4. *Reproducing*
5. *Growing*
6. *Eliminating*
7. *Ingesting*
8. *Living*

The Flow of Blood Through the Heart (Teacher's Key)

For the numbers within the heart, place arrows in the appropriate direction to show correct blood flow. For the numbers outside the heart, describe what activity is occurring corresponding to the number in the heart.

1 Blood from body enters right atrium through superior vena cava and inferior vena cava

2 Blood enters right ventricle through tricuspid valve

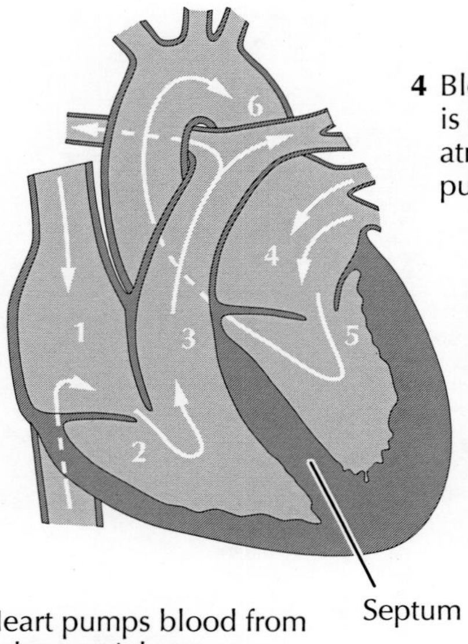

3 Heart pumps blood from right ventricle to pulmonary trunk, which carries blood to the lungs where oxygen is absorbed

4 Blood carrying oxygen is returned to the left atrium through the pulmonary veins

5 Blood enters left ventricle through bicuspid valve

6 Heart pumps blood from left ventricle to aorta, which carries blood to the body

The Circulatory System (Teacher's Key)

Label the appropriate veins and arteries. Write a brief paragraph on the benefits of having a healthy circulatory system. You may use the back of this worksheet.

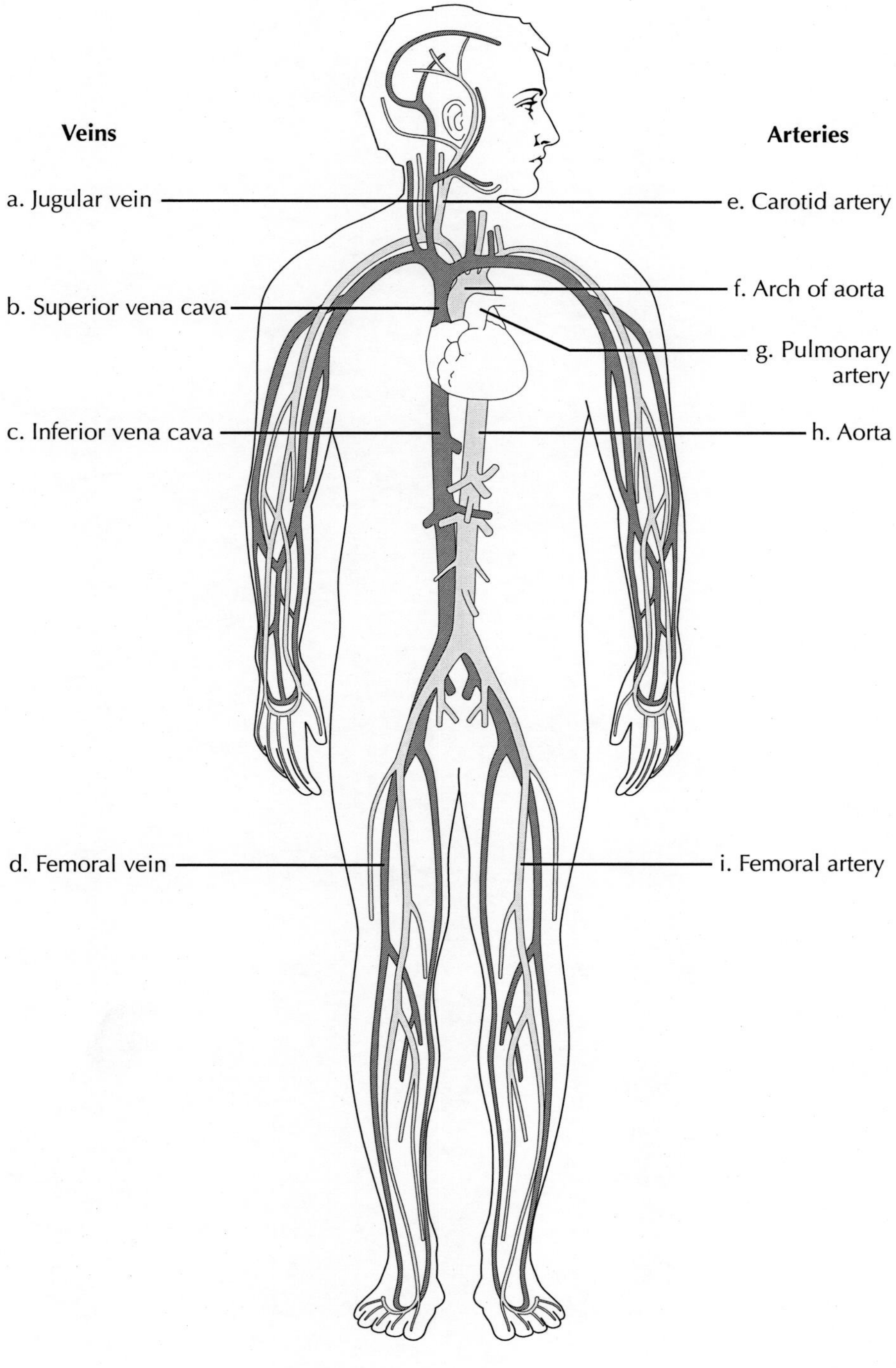

The Respiratory System (Teacher's Key)

Label the correct parts of the respiratory system. Write a brief paragraph explaining how a person can properly care for his/her reaspiratory system. You may use the back of this worksheet.

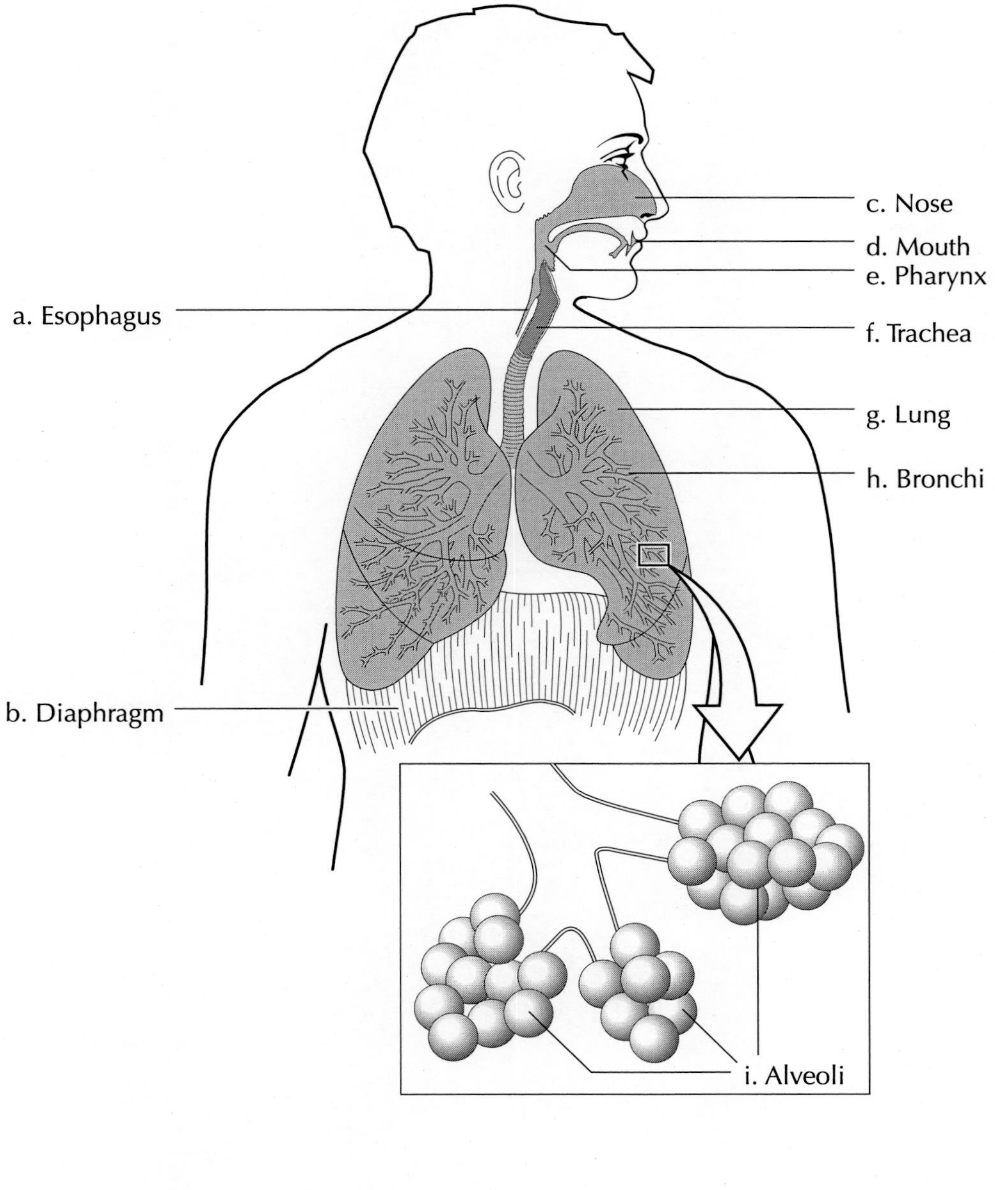

The Skeletal System (Teacher's Key)

Label the appropriate parts of the skeletal system. Using the back of this worksheet, write a brief paragraph describing the four types of bones in the body.

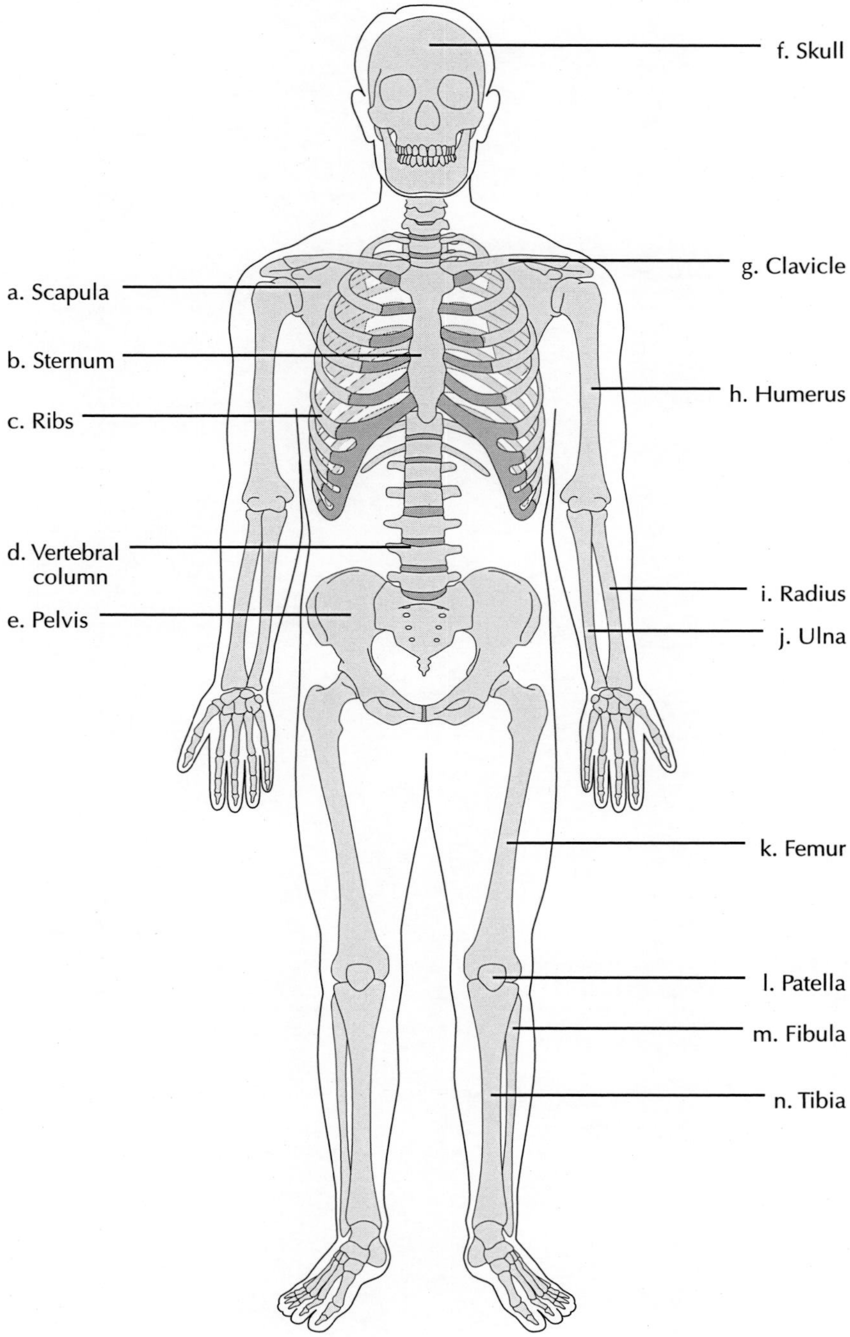

The Muscular System (Teacher's Key)

Label the parts of the muscular system, and on the back of this worksheet write a brief paragraph on the benefits of exercise to the muscular system.

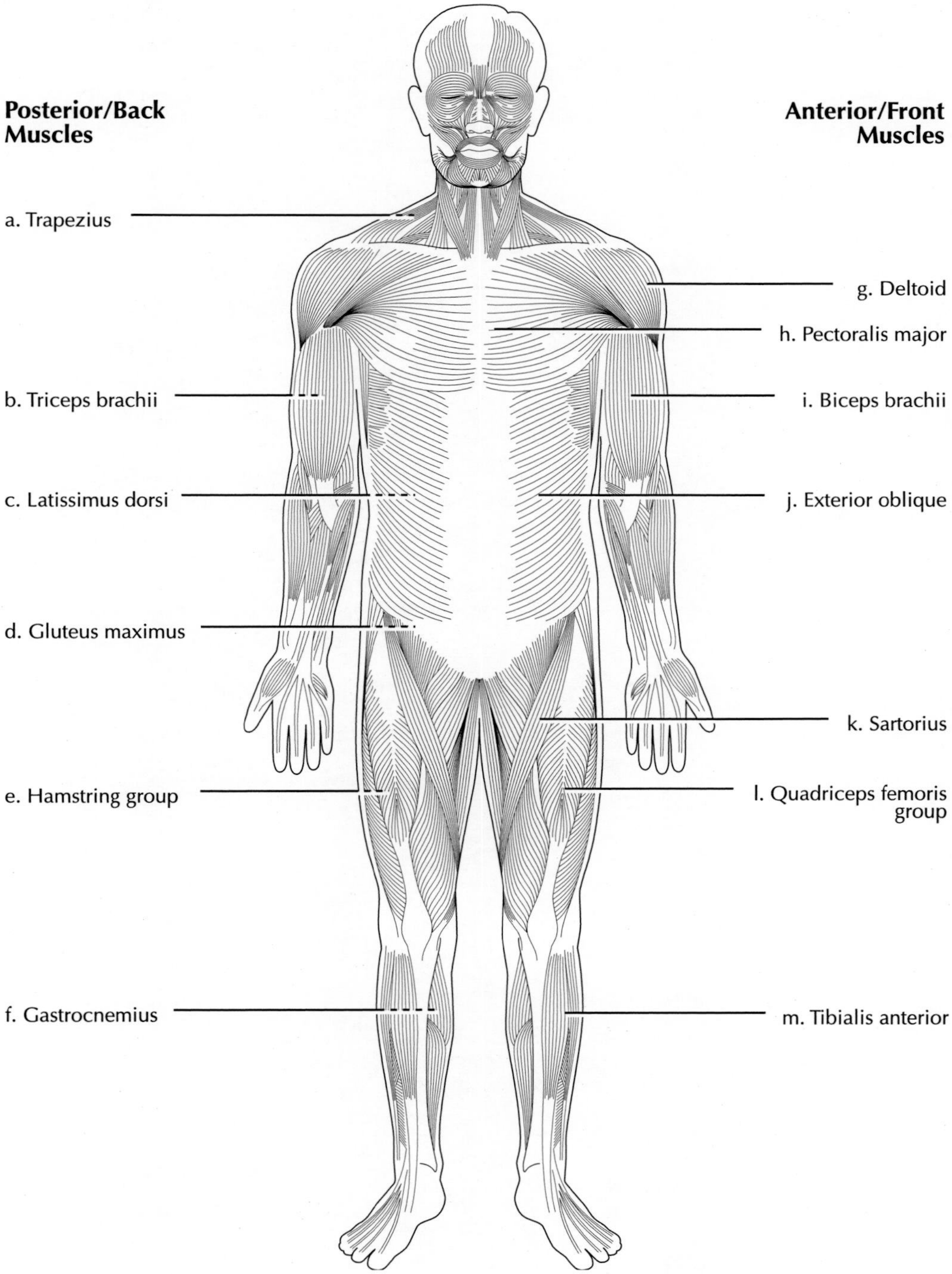

The Digestive and Excretory Systems (Teacher's Key)

Label the parts of the digestive and excretory systems. Using the back of this worksheet, write a brief paragraph on the benefits of having healthy digestive and excretory systems.

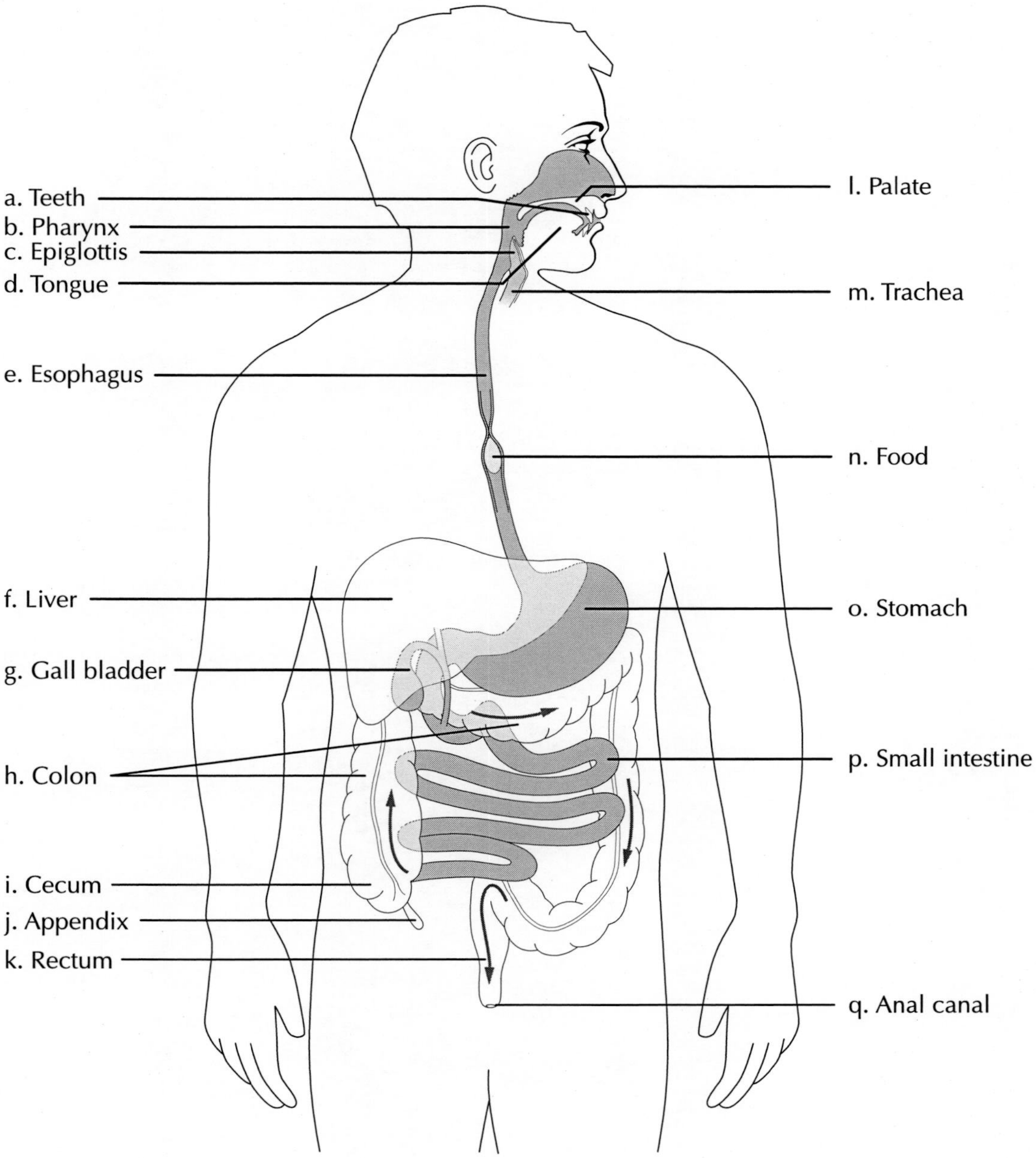

The Endocrine System (Teacher's Key)

Label the appropriate parts of the male and female endocrine systems.

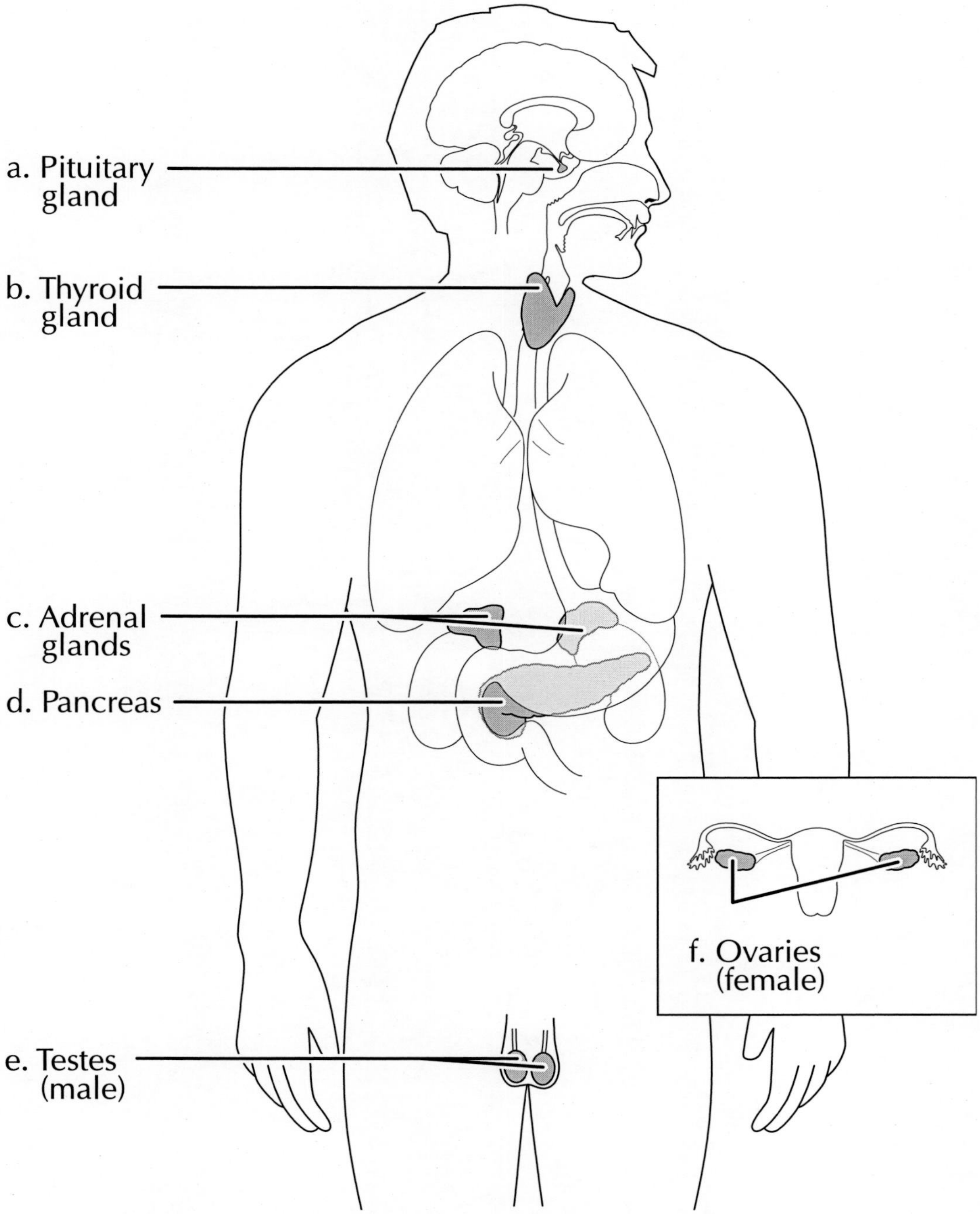

Name ______________________ Date ____________

Vocabulary (Teacher's Key)

Define the following terms:

1. Balanced diet: *making food choices that include a wide variety from all that God has given you in nature*
2. Empty calorie: *foods that have no nutritive value*
3. Proteins: *amino acids used by the body to build cells and tissues*
4. Carbohydrates: *sugars and starches that the body uses for energy*
5. Fats: *concentrated sources of energy that provide twice as much fuel as carbohydrates*
6. RDA: *Recommended Daily Allowance*
7. Anorexia: *a self-induced starvation characterized by an intense fear of gaining weight and becoming fat*
8. Bulimia: *a pattern of "binging" (eating large amounts of food) and "purging" (self-induced vomiting or laxative abuse) which may or may not be accompanied by weight loss*
9. Chronic overeating: *the habit of taking in more food than your body needs*
10. Metabolic rate: *the speed at which your body burns calories*
11. Vegetarian diet: *a diet that excludes animal products*
12. Diet: *all the foods you choose to eat on a regular basis*

Part Two

Write the word in the blank that fits best. Choose your words from the list below.

1. When Roger realized he was over 20% beyond his ideal body weight he knew he had become *obese* and needed to make some changes to reverse the problem.
2. It was recommended that I take a supplement to insure I get a proper balance of *vitamins* and *minerals*.
3. Our energy use and needs are measured in heat units called *calories*.
4. To minimize the risk of heart disease doctors can monitor the levels of *cholesterol* in our blood and make recommendations to lower the concentration should it become too high.
5. The *nutrients* in the foods we eat insure that we receive needed supplies of vitamins, minerals and fuel for energy and restoration.
6. Some vitamins pass through the system easily and are not stored and so are called *water-soluble*.

(cont. ➻)

7. Other vitamins can be stored in the body and can even cause harm should the concentrations become too high. These substances are _fat-soluble_.
8. _Essential amino acids_ are a group of eight substances your body needs for growth and maintenance that it does not produce on its own and must be contained in the foods you eat.
9. I knew I was heavier than recommended for my age, sex and size and so faced the fact that I had slowly become _overweight_.
10. The fatty substances less likely to raise blood cholesterol levels are _unsaturated fats_.
11. The bacon grease that congeals in the bottom of the frying pan, and one of many substances that will contribute to an increased cholesterol level in the blood is a graphic example of a _saturated fat_.

Nutrients	Unsaturated fats
Overweight	Cholesterol
Minerals	Fat soluble
Essential amino acids	Vitamins
Water soluble	Saturated fat
Obese	Calories

Vocabulary (Teacher's Key)

Crossword

ACROSS

2. The relationship between your fat and lean muscle body weight (two words)
6. The condition of your heart, lungs, and blood vessels to provide oxygenated blood to your whole body (two words)

DOWN

1. The power of your mind and body to work together to their highest possible level
3. Your muscles' strength and endurance (two words)
4. Short bursts of physical energy without the use of much oxygen, e.g., sprinting, golf, weight training
5. Physical activities you can do for as long as you are able, e.g., tennis, golf (two words)
7. Decrease in size and strength of muscles
8. When your muscles demand more oxygen than normal
10. The ability to move your joints and muscles through a full range of motion

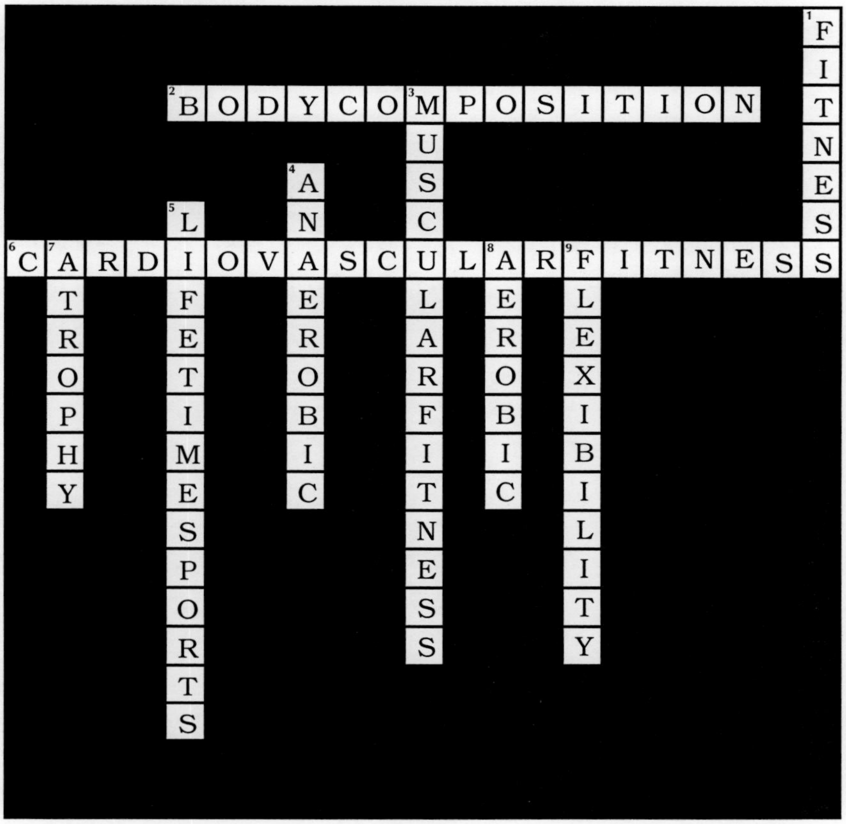

Vocabulary (Teacher's Key)

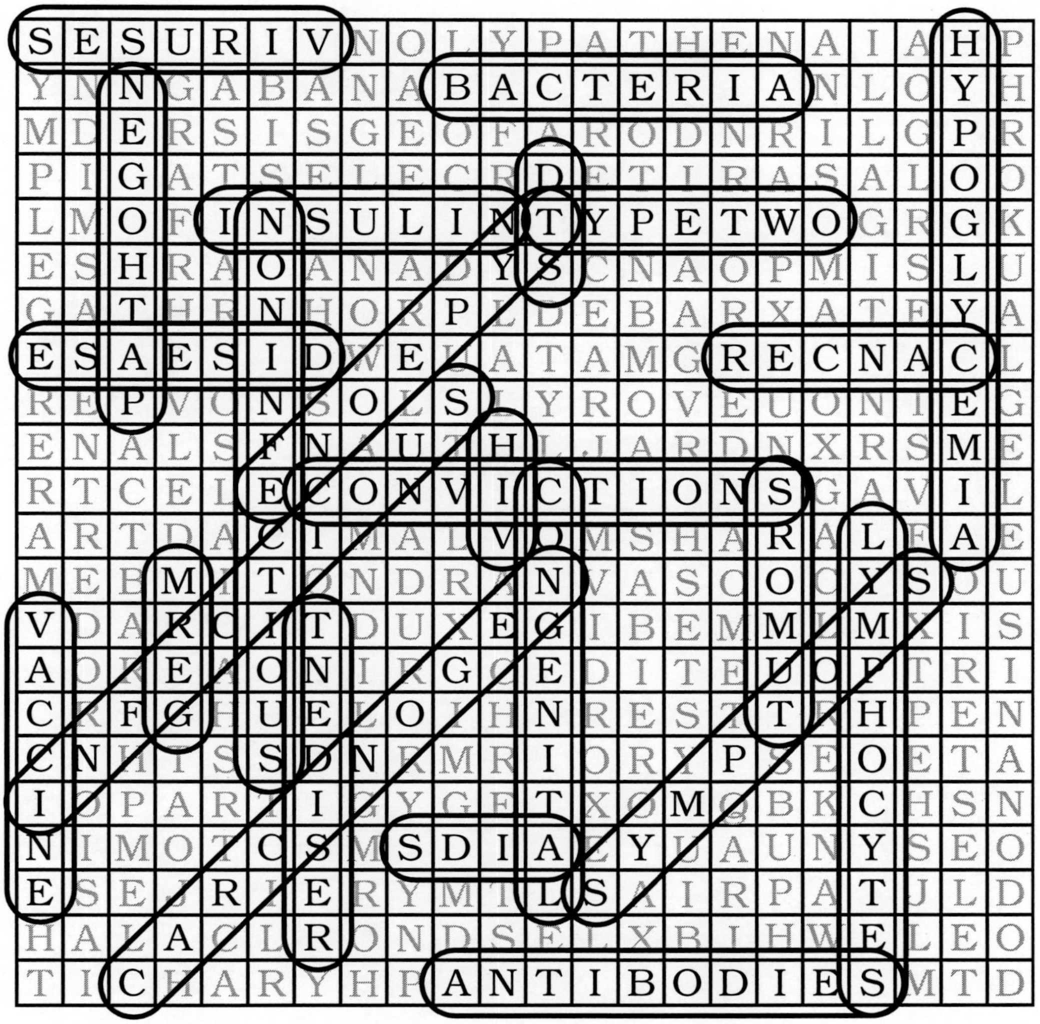

Note that definition number one has two correct answers and both are in the answer field.

1. germ, pathogen
2. carcinogen
3. congenital
4. AIDS
5. insulin
6. hypoglycemia
7. cancer
8. type two
9. tumors
10. convictions
11. type one
12. HIV
13. lymphocytes
14. symptoms
15. disease
16. infectious
17. vaccine
18. non-infectious
19. STD
20. antibodies
21. bacteria
22. viruses
23. resident

The War on Disease (Teacher's Key)

The medical field consists of doctors who have specialized areas of study. Match the field of the specialization on the left with its corresponding description on the right.

A Oncology
F Hematology
J Cardiology
I Chiropractic
N Dermatology
D Gastroenterology
O Otolaryngology
E Geriatrics
P Pediatrics
R Ophthalmology
M Osteopathic
H Obstetrics
L Endocrinology
Q Neurology
C Nephrology
K Psychiatry
B Podiatry
G Naturopathy

A. The study of the causes, development, characteristics, and treatment of cancer

B. The branch of medicine that deals with the diseases and malfunctions of the foot and its related structures

C. The medical specialty concerned with the normal functioning of the kidneys

D. The study of the digestive system and diseases and disorders affecting it

E. The medical specialty concerned with care of the elderly

F. The study of blood and disorders of the blood

G. A form of alternative medicine based on the principle that disease is due to the accumulation of waste products and toxins in the body. Practitioners believe that health is maintained by avoiding anything artificial or unnatural in the diet.

H. The branch of medicine concerned with pregnancy, childbirth, and postnatal care

I. A theory of healing based on the belief that disease results from a lack of normal nerve function with physical manipulation and adjustment of the spine for therapy

J. The study of the function of the heart

K. The branch of medicine concerned with the study, prevention, and treatment of mental illness

L. The study of the glands and the hormones they secrete

M. The diagnosis and treatment that recognizes the role of the musculoskeletal system in the healthy functioning of the human body

N. The study of skin diseases.

O. The study of the eyes, ears, nose, and throat.

P. The branch of study concerned with the growth and development of children

Q. The study of the nervous system and its disorders

R. The study of the eye and the diagnosis and treatment of its disorders

BIBLE STUDY

My Convictions
Part 1 (Teacher's Key)

The faith that you have, have as your own conviction before God.
Romans 14:22, NAS

What Are Some of Your Present Convictions?

The apostle Paul wanted the Christians in Rome to have personal convictions. A conviction is a strong, settled, and sincere belief that something's right. Do you have any convictions right now? Read the following "I" statements and circle each one for which you presently hold a strong conviction. Please be honest. Don't mark the statements that you feel you "should" have convictions about, but only the ones that you presently do hold strong convictions about.

- ✞ I believe that the God of the Bible exists.
- ✞ I sincerely think that Jesus healed the sick and did miracles.
- ✞ I'm convinced that Jesus died on the cross for my sins.
- ✞ I'm persuaded that Jesus rose from the dead.
- ✞ I have a strong opinion that non-Christians need Jesus Christ.
- ✞ I know for sure that I'm a born-again Christian and am going to heaven.

Identifying Convictions from Scripture and Beginning to Form Your Own

Describe in your own words what type of conviction(s) would be appropriate to develop from the following verses. Give one reason why you agree or disagree with each one.

1. *Psalm* 15:1,3, "Lord, who may abide in your tabernacle?...He who does not backbite with his tongue..."
   A conviction against: *backbiting*
   I agree/disagree with this because:

2. *Genesis* 6:11
   A conviction against: *corruption* and *violence*
   I agree/disagree with this because:

3. *Matthew* 6:6, "But you, when you pray, go into your room..."
   A conviction about: *prayer*
   I agree/disagree with this because:

(*cont.* ➸)

4. *Ephesians* 6:1-3
A conviction about: *teens respecting and obeying their parents*
I agree/disagree with this because:

5. *Ephesians* 5:18, "And be not drunk with wine in which is dissipation [waste]; but be filled with the Spirit..."
A conviction against: *drunkenness*, along with a conviction for: *walking in the Spirit*
I agree/disagree with this because:

Vocabulary (Teacher's Key)

Next to each of the seven words below, write the corresponding letter of the definition from the bottom of the page that best describes the word. Not all of the definitions apply to the words from the list.

Pride ___*B*___

Self-esteem ___*J*___

Personal identity ___*C*___

Jealousy ___*G*___

Mature ___*K*___

Character ___*H*___

Confident ___*E*___

a. Feelings that we have not received our fair share

b. A belief that we are better than we really are

c. An understanding of who we are through Christ

d. Suspicion that others are intent on undermining our efforts

e. An absence of feelings of inferiority or feeling "less than"

f. A mocking, cartoon-like representation of a person's efforts

g. The feeling of resentment toward another person for a talent or possession they have that you wish for yourself

h. Who you really are, even when no one is observing you

i. A fear that we may be overlooked for a promotion or award

j. The way you feel about yourself

k. To grow spiritually, socially, emotionally, mentally and physically

l. To belittle the efforts of others; to cause them humiliation

How to Replace Worry with Faith and Peace (Teacher's Key)

BIBLE STUDY

1. **Know what worry is and learn how to recognize it in yourself.**

   How does the dictionary define the term worry?

   Webster defines worry as: to feel uneasy or anxious; torment oneself with or suffer from disturbing thoughts. Fret.

   How can you tell you might be worrying about certain things?

   Upset stomach, loss or increase in appetite, feelings of anxiousness, inability to sleep at night, easily irritated by things, feeling fearfulness or increased anxiety over things, binging on food/snacks.

2. **Write down some of the areas in your life that you are worried about right now.**

   Some answers may include: boys, girls, grades, relationship with parents, illness, death of a loved one, not fitting in socially.

3. **Read what Jesus said about the basic necessities of life and how His words might also apply to your own areas of worry which you listed above.**

   According to Jesus, what are the three things that you don't have to worry about?

   (1) food (2) drink (3) clothes.

   Do you think this includes other areas of your life as well?

   Yes.

   What are the three reasons that Jesus gives as to why Christians don't have to worry?

   (1) that one's life and body are more important than food or clothing

   (2) that human beings are more valuable to God than the birds or lilies which He already takes care of sovereignly

   (3) that worrying can't add any more days/time to your life

   What does Jesus say is, oftentimes, at the heart of an unbeliever's worry and focus on obtaining the material necessities of life? *Pride*

   What does Jesus say are the two conditions (the "if's") of God sovereignly taking care of believers?

   (1) if they give him first place in their lives

   (2) if they live as He wants them to live

(*cont.* ➸)

Why would Jesus warn you against "borrowing trouble"?

Because each day has enough "evil" or bad things of its own without adding some more from tomorrow.

4. Know what faith is and appreciate how it increases in your life.

How does the dictionary define the term faith?

Webster defines faith as confidence and trust in a person or thing.

In your own words, explain what faith means to you:

Answers will vary.

5. Read Paul's secret to a worry-free life and begin to practice it.

What does Paul say you should do to replace worry with peace?

Pray about everything.

How does Paul actually describe the answer to the above question?

"tell God your needs and don't forget to thank Him for His answers"

What benefit will come to your thoughts and your emotions ("your hearts") when you practice the answer to the first question?

Protection of your inner peace,quietness, and rest

Choose one of the benefits from the above question and define it from the dictionary.

1. *Peace is harmony, freedom from inner worry, anxiety, and annoyance; deep faith and trust in God's love and control.*
2. *Rest is calmness of spirit.*
3. *Quietness is not being filled with inner turmoil so you can hear God's voice.*

How can it apply to your life?

How to Overcome Negative Self-Talk (Teacher's Key)

Listed below are ten statements which are examples of negative self-talk recordings you might be familiar with. Each is a reflection of one or more of the following untruths:

a. "I must meet certain standards to feel good about myself."

b. "I must be accepted by certain people (significant others in my life) to feel good about myself."

c. "Those who fail (including myself) are unworthy of love and deserve to be blamed and condemned."

d. "I am what I am. I cannot change. I am hopeless. I will never amount to anything."

Study the following statements. Ask yourself: "What false belief(s) does this statement represent?" Beside each statement, place the letter of one or more of the false beliefs from the above list that best correspond(s) with the statement. Answers may overlap or differ slightly.

b 1. "My sister is right. I'll never do anything right. I'm such a failure."

d 2. "I'm so undisciplined. I'll never be able to accomplish anything."

d 3. "I will never be able to trust God."

b 4. "No one important in my class wants to hang out with me."

d 5. "I don't have any musical ability like my friends. I don't do anything well."

c 6. "I failed math. I'll always be stupid."

d 7. "I can't overcome this sin."

c 8. "I really don't deserve friends anyway. I'm such a loser."

a 9. "I will never be able to please my parents."

c 10. "No one will ever like me. I am so ugly."

Grow in Openness to God (Teacher's Key)

Steven had the heart attitude which cared more about what God thought than what others thought. How can you learn to view God as your true friend?

1. What makes someone a true friend?
   A friend is concerned about what is important to his/her friend.

2. How might a person be a true friend to God?
   Being God's friend means that you care about what is important to Him.

3. What are some things that you think are important to God?

4. How can you show God that you care about what is important to Him?
   By reading the Bible and learning what He thinks is important and trying to do it.

In the Bible, God reveals what He thinks is important. What God values often differs from what society values.

5. What things does society see as valuable?
   Externals such as performance, appearance, popularity, wealth, success, being "cool" and in the "in-group".

6. Write out *I Samuel* 13:14; 16:7.
   The Lord has sought out a man after his own heart...Man looks at the outward appearance, but the Lord looks on the heart.

7. In contrast to what society values, what is God concerned about in you?
   The heart attitude

8. Write out *II Chronicles* 16:9.
   The eyes of the Lord range throughout the earth to strengthen those whose hearts are fully committed to Him.

Vocabulary (Teacher's Key)

Write the missing word in the blank in each sentence from the list below. Not all of the words from the list apply to one of the sentences.

1. David made a list of steps he would need to accomplish over time in order to achieve his ___*long-term goal*___.
2. Terri knew that her questions had been too personal and invasive. She felt that she had crossed a ___*boundary*___ her friend had established for herself.
3. Ron knew if he allowed himself to be drawn into the argument, it would ___*distract*___ him from the project he was trying to complete.
4. It took all of her ___*self-control*___ to avoid saying something hurtful after what had happened between her and her sister.
5. His ___*short-term goal*___ would be put into motion soon by following through on the plans he had made for the immediate future.
6. In order to make a list of plans and follow through in our lives, it is important that we have a clear understanding of our ultimate ___*goal*___.

Repentance	Acquisition
Long-term goal	Self-control
Goal	Boundary
Limitations	Short-term goal
Forgiveness	Distract

Identifying and Facing Your Fears (Teacher's Key)

Pat's Story

1. What did Pat fear in this story? *He feared disappointing God.*
2. How do you think that Pat's eventually positive experience of confession and restitution (his returning the skateboard) will affect Pat the next time he needs to confess a sin to God?

   It will help him open up to God more quickly and easily.

Angie's Story

1. What did Angie fear in this incident?

   She feared failing her English test and getting her parents mad. The fear of failure. The fear of disappointing her parents.
2. What did Angie choose to allow her fear to do to her?

   To do something that she had never done before: cheat on an exam.

Tony's Story

1. What did Tony fear Pete would do to him if he didn't go out to the woods with him and the guys?

   Tony feared that Pete would no longer be his friend; that he would reject him. The fear of rejection.
2. If you had been Tony, what would you have done with your fear about Pete instead of going out into the woods?

   Answers will vary. I would have let my fear (respect) for God be greater than my fear of Pete's rejecting me. I would have felt badly about possibly losing Pete's friendship, but I would have told him that what he was doing I couldn't do.

Chris' Story

1. What was Chris' fear?

   Chris' fear was that Janet and his Dad might get a divorce just like his Dad and Mom did. The fear of a painful past experience being repeated.
2. What was Jack's response to Chris' fear?

   Jack told Chris that he shouldn't have his feelings of fear about his engagement to Janet. The key word here is "shouldn't". It was perfectly normal for Chris to have this fear.

(*cont.* ➻)

3. If you had been Chris, how would Jack's comments to you about your fear have made you feel?

   Answers will vary. Jack's comments would have made me feel dumb; maybe even guilty for having such fears.

4. If you had been Jack, would you have changed your comment to Chris? If so, how would you have re-worded it?

   Answers will vary. I would not have criticized Chris' feelings of fear because there was nothing wrong with them. I would have told him that I understood his feelings, and found some reason to agree with them, so that he could begin to accept the situation more easily.

What is True Success? (Teacher's Key)

Look up the following Bible references and write them in the space provided. Answer the questions that follow each verse. Also, summarize what that verse means to you and how you can apply it to your life.

Proverbs **28:6** *Better to be poor and honest than rich and a cheater. (TLB)*

Answer: The key subject is riches. It is more important to God for a person to have integrity and good character than to have lots of money which he obtains through illegal means.

1. Do you know of anyone who obtained their money by lying, cheating, stealing, or some other illegal means? If so, who? How did they make their money? *Yes, organized criminals, drugs.*
2. What role, if any, do you feel that God had in the obtaining of their wealth? *None. The devil helped them get the money through sinful and dishonest ways.*
3. How can this verse apply to your own personal life?

Proverbs **22:4** *True humility and respect for the Lord lead a man to riches, honor, and long life. (TLB)*

Answer: The key subject is humble fear of God. Being aware of your weaknesses, obedient, and reverent to God will many times bring a person the things that most people want.

1. What does the word honor mean? What is the difference between the human honor that our culture gives to people and the honor which God gives? *Honor means praise, attention and reward. The difference is that our culture knows little or nothing of giving honor to people's love for the poor, sacrificial giving to the destitute, small efforts to share Christ's kindness except when it is financially or politically rewarding or expedient.*
2. John the Baptist died at a young age because Herod had him beheaded in prison. How could his short life still be considered a success? *His life was still a total success because he knew the will of God for his life—preaching repentance for sins—and did it wholeheartedly.*
3. How can this verse apply to your own personal life?

I Corinthians **9:25** *To win the contest you must deny yourselves many things that would keep you from doing your best. An athlete goes to all this trouble just to win a blue ribbon or a silver cup, but we do it for a heavenly reward that never disappears. (TLB)*

(cont. ➻)

Answer: The key subject is temporary, earthly rewards vs. eternal, heavenly rewards. God will reward those who deny themselves everything that stands in the way of God being first in their lives. He will reward those who faithfully serve Him with the experience of His wonderful presence—not only on earth but also in heaven.

1. Have you ever had a goal for which you had to give up something else to obtain? If so, what was your goal and what did you have to give up? *My goal was being on the volleyball team. I had to give up spending every afternoon having fun with my friends.*

2. Have you ever received a ribbon or trophy for placing in some athletic event? If so, what was the event and where did you place? Do you still have the ribbon or trophy? Do you think that you'll still have it ten years from now? What could this teach you about earthly rewards? *Yes, for the 100 yard dash I won a blue ribbon. No, I don't still have it. Not if I don't have it now. Earthly rewards are temporary and pass away with time.*

3. How can this verse apply to your own personal life?

Steps to Making Wise Decisions (Teacher's Key)

Introduction

Write out *Proverbs* 9:10-11:

For the reverence and fear of God are basic to all wisdom. Knowing God results inear understanding. For by me your days will be multiplied, and years of life will be added to you. (NKJ)

1. Why do you think that knowing God results in every other kind of understanding?

   Answers will vary. God is sovereign and involved in all areas of life.

2. How can having more wisdom make your life more fruitful and profitable?

   Answers will vary. With wisdom from God, you'll be able to find His will and His will is what makes us fruitful and successful.

How to Make Wise Decisions

1. Gather Information: Do Your Homework!

Your Goal: To find as many facts and ideas as possible about a problem to be solved or an idea to be investigated.

Jim's Story

A. What information might Jim need to help him with this difficult decision?

How important was the computer game to him? Was he willing to take the time to save the money again?

B. Who might Jim talk to to gain more wisdom about his decision about the game?

His parent(s), teachers, counselors, youth pastor.

C. Do you think that Jim should tell Josh his dilemma? Why or why not?

If no, because it might hurt Josh's feelings. If yes, because it would give Josh a good reason Jim couldn't go with him.

D. Do you think God really cares how Jim spends his money? How might Jim pray for wisdom concerning this decision?

Yes, God cares about Jim's money. He might ask Gos for peace about whether to go or not.

2. Get Input from God.

Your Goal: Give God the opportunity to reveal His thoughts about a problem to be solved or an idea to be investigated.

(*cont.* ➻)

Rebecca's Story

A. What kind of information does Rebecca need to know about her decision concerning Amy? Does she need any further information?

Rebecca doesn't need any more information since she already feels uncomfortable with Amy's social life and interests.

B. Who might Rebecca talk to so as to gain more wisdom about her decision about Amy?

Her parent(s), teacher(s), counselor(s), youth pastor.

C. If Rebecca decides to cut off her friendship with Amy, what consequences should Rebecca be prepared for?

To be rejected by Amy and, possibly, her friends.

D. If Rebecca decides not to cut off her friendship with Amy, what consequences should Rebecca be prepared for?

Amy pressuring/teasing Rebecca about boys and parties.

E. Is there anything else that Rebecca might do to help her with this decision?

Talk to Amy about her two concerns.

F. How might Rebecca pray for wisdom concerning this difficult decision?

To help you answer this question, first read *James* 1:5-6 in *The Living Bible.*

1. According to *James* 1:5, if Rebecca wants to know what God wants her to do, what should she do?

   Ask Him!

2. What does God say He will do if Rebecca asks Him?

   He will gladly tell her.

3. From this verse, does it seem that God would want to keep His thoughts about her situation from her or to tell Rebecca?

   No, God would want to tell her what He wants her to do.

4. What kind of attitude would be best for Rebecca to have when she asked God about her circumstance with Amy?

   Ask in faith, believing that He wants my best, expectantly.

5. If Rebecca didn't ask in faith, what might happen to her mind and her ultimate decision?

   It will be hard for her to make a decision because she will be moved by every bit of circumstance, advice, and feelings. Then her decision may not be what God had intended for her.

(*cont.* ➻)

Steps to Making Wise Decisions (Teacher's Key cont.)

6. How else might God speak to her other than in her prayer time?

   Through wise counselors who know her and the situation.
   Through reading her Bible and listening for anything to "jump out at her".
   Being quiet before God and waiting patiently for an answer.
   Through circumstances that line up with what she's feeling in her heart.

3. Make Your Decision.

Your Goal: To make the best possible choice about what to believe or do.

A. What might be the possible outcome if you procrastinated or waited too long to make your decision?

By waiting too long, you actually make a decision by not making a decision. You miss a deadline and you may miss an opportunity.

B. If after gathering information and praying about it, you still do not know what to do, what might you do?

Choosing not to choose is an option. If I can take longer I will keep praying until I get an answer. If I still don't feel comfortable with a decision, maybe not deciding is actually a better choice. I will face the consequences of choosing not to make a decision based on the information I gathered (or lack of information).

C. If you have not done your homework, and have not taken the time to get input from God concerning your decision, what might be the possible outcome?

By making a decision on little information and no input from God, the decision could be a poor choice and have negative consequences.

4. Evaluate Your Decision.

Your Goal: To learn from your decision.

A. Imagine that Jim decided to go to the game with Josh. Why would it be important for Jim to evaluate his decision when he returned from the game?

To see if he still felt in his heart that he made the right decision.

B. If Rebecca decided to cut off her relationship with Amy, what do you think Rebecca might learn from that decision?

That teens who live purely get teased. That talking to friends about spiritual concerns is worth it.

Vocabulary (Teacher's Key)

C	H	O	K	M	N	O	N	V	E	R	B	A	L	E	S	B	P
A	O	D	I	S	R	E	S	P	E	C	T	I	R	N	L	N	A
I	N	F	A	T	U	A	T	I	O	N	H	T	O	D	L	O	R
H	O	H	R	N	T	S	L	M	A	L	K	I	T	O	A	I	O
G	P	A	T	E	C	H	A	Y	A	H	T	E	Z	N	W	T	K
E	H	D	I	S	E	V	A	M	G	U	G	D	I	T	S	A	E
V	A	I	F	H	P	A	M	O	T	E	Q	E	V	A	U	C	T
I	N	P	I	H	S	N	O	I	T	A	L	E	R	J	O	I	H
T	I	H	C	N	E	H	T	C	A	I	H	S	E	M	Y	N	N
I	M	C	I	O	R	S	A	E	A	R	O	T	A	H	E	U	O
S	E	E	A	R	B	G	L	D	O	H	L	L	T	G	R	M	I
O	V	Y	L	U	O	L	A	S	H	I	K	A	A	D	E	M	T
P	I	H	S	D	N	E	I	R	F	U	P	T	B	O	H	O	A
S	G	E	D	U	L	A	C	E	T	M	I	H	P	R	T	C	T
E	R	H	B	Y	N	H	O	H	E	V	A	R	A	S	E	W	U
Y	O	A	R	U	V	E	S	C	E	A	Z	T	E	N	K	V	P
R	F	N	O	Y	I	Z	T	H	T	E	R	E	H	P	I	T	E
D	A	A	T	H	K	O	N	A	H	C	E	G	N	E	V	E	R

1. social
2. friendship
3. relationship
4. substitutions
5. artificial
6. communication
7. verbal
8. nonverbal
9. walls
10. infatuation
11. positive
12. negative
13. respect
14. disrespect
15. reputation
16. revenge
17. forgive
18. empathy

Friendship (Teacher's Key)

BIBLE STUDY

Read the following verses about friendship and answer the questions which follow.

1. "A mirror reflects a man's face, but what he is really like is shown by the kind of friends he chooses." *Proverbs* **27:19 (TLB)**

a. What are some of the ways that you normally use to try to tell what kind of a person someone really is?

Answers will vary. We "size up" others by their looks, the car they drive, their attitude, the way they relate to others, the amount of money they have, the neighborhood they live in, the clothes they wear, the way they do their hair, etc.

b. Why are the above ways not perfect methods?

They don't always work because someone can appear on the outside to be totally different than they are on the inside.

c. What similarities or common interests do you have with your closest friends?

Answers will vary. We enjoy the same sports, activities, kind of jokes, talking about the same kinds of things, riding bikes, watching TV, etc.

d. We can refer to what the above verse says about friendship as The Friendship Mirror. Do you feel that The Friendship Mirror can be an accurate way to discern a person's inner character? Why or why not?

Answers will vary. We enjoy another person's company because we accept each other, share common interests and don't criticize each other. The closer we are to people, the more we have to be similar to them on the inside. True intimacy is based on closeness of the inner heart or core of someone's life.

2. "A true friend is always loyal, and a brother [or, sister] is born to help in time of need." *Proverbs* **17:17 (TLB)**

a. If there are friends that are "true", do you think that there are also friends that are "false"? If so, what qualities would a "false" friend have that you wouldn't like?

Answers will vary. A false friend would talk badly about us behind our backs, pretend, not reall want to help us when we need help, etc.

b. Write down your definition of loyalty.

Loyalty is faithfulness and allegiance to one's government, promises, responsibilities, and friends.

(cont. ➸)

c. Which of your friends have been really loyal to you? What did they do to prove or show their loyalty to you?

Answers will vary. Mary and Dave were really loyal to me. They supported me when others put me down; they listened to me when I needed to talk; they didn't criticize me when I made a mistake; they encouraged me when I felt down, etc.

d. Explain one time that you really felt like you needed the help of your friend(s). If one of your true friends helped you, please explain how.

Answers will vary. E.g., I really needed help one time when my best friend said that she didn't like me anymore. Mary helped me by listening to me and encouraging me to see all of the positive qualities that I have to offer a friend.

Friendships (Teacher's Key):
Understanding God's Blessings with Different Kinds of Friends

1. Is the way that we judge others by the kind of people with whom they spend a significant amount of time always accurate? Why or why not?

   The answer is "no" because Jesus spent time with people of bad reputation because His motive was to help them get closer to God.

2. If a Christian teenager began to wear the same kind of jeans as one of his non-Christian friends, would that automatically mean that his or her heart was being turned away from Jesus?

   The answer is "no" because just because a teen wears the same kind of clothes as another teen, it does not mean that they have the same values or beliefs.

1. What do you think a couple of reasons might be that God would like you to have some non-Christian friends?

   The answers will vary. To show them the love of God. To witness to them about Christ. To learn a skill from them. To show them that Christians are normal people. To bring families closer together.

2. Become aware of your own limitations and weaknesses. Are you strong enough to have a friendship with another person? Are you a positive influence upon them? Are they a positive influence upon you? E.g., we wouldn't recommend that a recovering alcoholic live next door to a bar because he knows that alcohol is a real weakness for him. What are some of your own personal areas of weakness? Why might God tell you not to have a friendship with someone in light of what your weaknesses are?

   Answers will vary. Example 1: My weakness is TV. If I was a good friend with someone who also had a problem with TV, I might watch the wrong kind of shows together and also spend too much time "on the couch". Example 2: My weakness is anger. If I was a good friend with someone else who had a bad temper, then I might not learn to overcome my problem and we might get mad at each other all the time, not knowing how to resolve our conflicts.

Evaluating Hidden Motives In Friendships (Teacher's Key)

The following are a list of five common motives that may be influencing your friendships. Place the number for one or more of the following motivations that best describes the attitude behind the statement.

1. **Selfishness:** seeking only what you can get out of the friendship with no desire to give.
2. **Genuine acceptance:** choosing to be friends with someone just because of who they are.
3. **Fear:** acting out of a fear of rejection that you might not be accepted unless you do things to 'measure up'.
4. **Seeking approval:** choosing those who are in the "in crowd" as friends so you can belong to the most popular group.
5. **Genuine interest:** choosing a friend based upon your sincere interest in him/her as a person and having a mutual interest in one another's good.

__*4*__ "He is so popular with others, I want to be his friend, too."

__*1*__ "How can I benefit from being this person's friend?"

__*3*__ "All the cool guys smoke cigarettes. I really want them to like me, so I better start smoking."

__*1*__ "I heard the new guy in class has really rich parents; it would be great to be his friend."

__*4*__ "She is so popular with the boys; if I were her friend, maybe the boys would like me, too."

__*1 or 2*__ "He really seems to have his life together; what could he teach me if I got to know him?"

__*1*__ "He is so smart, if I become his friend, maybe he would help me with my homework."

__*1 or 2*__ "She seems to have a close relationship with God; if I got closer to her, maybe I could discover how she does it."

__*4*__ "Our youth group leaders always ask Jan to do things with them. If I become her friend, maybe I will be recognized, too."

__*5*__ "Steve has a lot going for him; I hope we stay friends; I want to see him reach God's full potential for his life."

__*4*__ "I heard the new girl in class was really popular in her old school; I wonder if she will like me."

__*3*__ "Only the people who are gifted musically get any attention in my youth group. I think I better take piano lessons."

The Power of Words (Teacher's Key)
James 3

Death and life are in the power of the tongue.
Proverbs 18:21

When was the last time you felt that someone hurt you? Did they hurt you through what they said to you or about you? Very probably. Do you remember the last time that someone made you feel really good? Did they do that through what they said to you or about you? Most probably. Words are very powerful! They bring life to others through encouraging them. But, they can also bring death to them by tearing them down in unkind ways. Read the following verses from *The Book of Proverbs*, the Bible's book of practical wisdom. This wisdom includes the best way to communicate with others so that everyone will feel understood and encouraged when we talk to them. List the one word from each verse that describes either the positive or the negative power in words.

Positive	Living Words	Negative	Deadly Words
1. *Proverbs* 10:20	*just*	1. *Proverbs* 12:19	*lying*
2. *Proverbs* 15:4	*wholesome*	2. *Proverbs* 25:23	*backbiting*
3. *Proverbs* 25:25	*soft*	3. *Proverbs* 28:23	*flattering*
4. *Proverbs* 31:26	*kind*	4. *Proverbs* 6:24	*sensual*

1. Write out *Matthew* 12:34.

   Out of the abundance of the heart, does the mouth speak.

2. In the above verse, from where does Jesus say your words come?

   Out of what fills your heart [inner person].

3. Write out *Proverbs* 21:23.

   Whoever guards his mouth and tongue keeps his soul [life] from troubles.

4. From the above verse, what should you do to try to keep yourself out of trouble?

   Watch what you say.

5. In what ways would guarding your words help you to keep out of trouble?

   It can prevent you from hurting other's feelings. It can help you to be honest. It can give you more friends and make you more popular. It can give you a good reputation.

Vocabulary (Teacher's Key)

Crossword

ACROSS

1. pink eye
3. masticate
7. sebum
10. keratin
12. subcutaneous
15. whitehead
16. tartar
17. gingivitis
18. head lice
20. cuticle
21. dandruff
22. follicle
23. periodontium

DOWN

1. pimple
2. dermis
4. sty
5. cavity
6. epidermis
8. astigmatism
9. acne
11. ingrown
13. blackhead
14. dermatologist
19. plaque

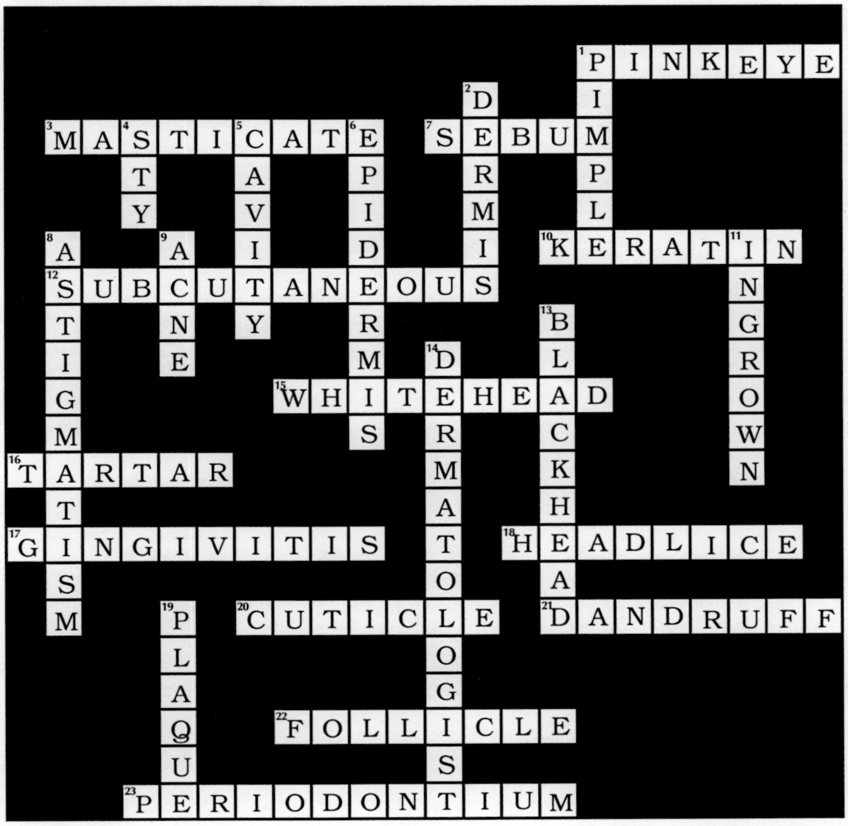

Match the Terms

1. If you have difficulty seeing things far away you are said to be <u>*H*</u>.
2. An advanced form of gum disease is <u>*G*</u>.
3. If your upper and lower teeth don't line up properly you have a <u>*A*</u>.
4. Another name for bad breath is <u>*E*</u>.
5. A procedure that uses braces to position the teeth correctly is called <u>*C*</u>.
6. A difficulty in seeing things that are close is called <u>*D*</u>.

The Importance of Personal Hygiene (Teacher's Key)

1. List three times that a person should wash their hands with soap and warm water during the day and why.

   a. Reason:

   b. Reason:

   c. Reason:

   For further information on sanitation and quarantine laws as revealed to Moses see: None of These Diseases by Dr. S. I. McMillan, Revell.

2. Have you ever not wanted to sit next to someone in class because they "smelled so badly"? If you want to have friends, you have to keep clean and fresh. List five deodorant/anti-perspirant products. Compare the ingredients. What is the main difference in ingredients?

   a. Ingredient(s):

   b. Ingredient(s):

   c. Ingredient(s):

   d. Ingredient(s):

   e. Ingredient(s):

   What's the difference between a deodorant and an anti-perspirant?

   Which do you think is necessary to use? Why?

   What causes body odor? *Body odor is caused by the presence of bacteria on the skin.*

   What do some people use as a natural alternative to these types of products? *Some natural products use salt.*

3. List three popular mouthwashes. What is their common ingredient?

   a. Ingredient(s):

   b. Ingredient(s):

   c. Ingredient(s):

   What natural products are used for the same purpose?

   What causes bad breath? *Bad breath is caused by: digestive problems, food caught in the teeth, bacteria in the mouth and on the teeth.*

The Parts of the Eye (Teacher's Key)

Label the parts of the eye.

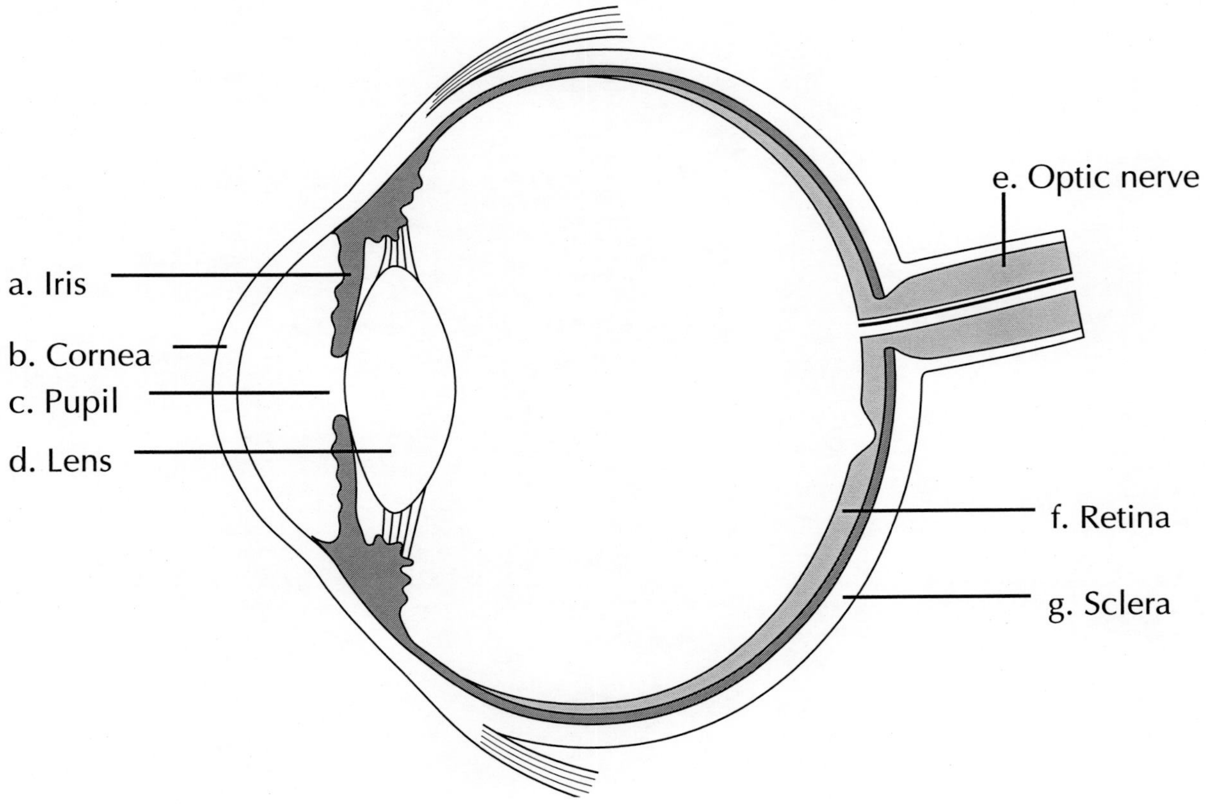

The Ear (Teacher's Key)

Label the parts of the ear.

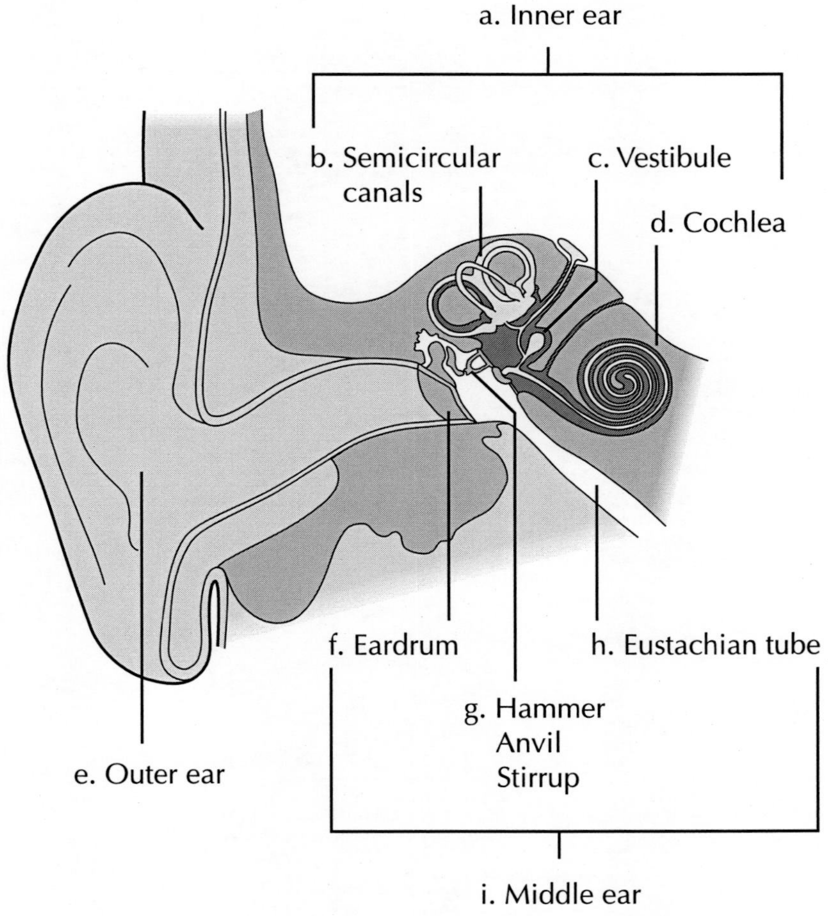

Vocabulary (Teacher's Key)

Crossword

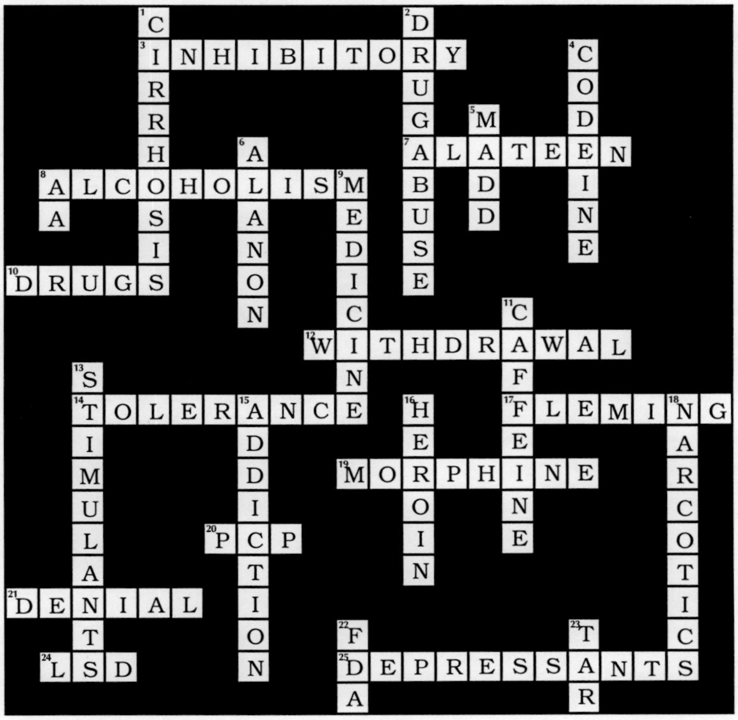

ACROSS
3. inhibitory
7. Alateen
8. alcoholism
10. drugs
12. withdrawal
14. tolerance
19. morphine
20. PCP
21. denial
24. LSD
25. depressants

DOWN
1. cirrhosis
2. drug abuse
4. codeine
5. MADD
6. Al-Anon
8. AA
9. medicine
11. caffeine
13. stimulants
15. addiction
16. heroin
17. Fleming
18. narcotics
22. FDA
23. tar

Match the Terms

1. Smoke that hangs in the air in an area where smokers have been smoking is called __C__ smoke.
2. The smoke that comes from the lit end of a cigarette is referred to as __F__ smoke.
3. __D__ is a poisonous gas produced by automobile engines and burning tobacco, among other sources.
4. Any reaction to a drug aside from the desired one is called a __J__.
5. Smoke that is inhaled and then exhaled by the smoker is __O__ smoke.
6. __G__ may be any of the three groupings shown in the questions above.
7. A group of drugs which cause the brain to form unreal images are the __E__.
8. A highly addictive, colorless, oily, highly toxic and addictive alkaloid compound obtained from tobacco is called __L__.
9. A drug sold only with a doctor's written order is a __A__ drug.
10. __M__ is a disease which disables the function of the alveoli (air sacs) of the lungs.
11. Drug compounds which may be purchased "over the counter" without the approval of a physician are called __B__ drugs.

What Does Gaining Freedom Mean to You? (Teacher's Key)

Put a check mark in the box(es) of every statement below which you feel most accurately describes your definition of "freedom". Under each of the several statements below, write an evaluation of each statement as to whether you feel each statement by itself is a Biblical and adequate description of freedom or not.

❑ Freedom means doing what I want to do just as long as it is legal.
Evaluation statement: *Not all legal things are moral, e.g., abortion in America.*

❑ Freedom means doing what I want just as long as I don't think that it's going to hurt anyone else.
Evaluation statement: *What you don't think is hurting someone else might certainly be hurting them.*

❑ Freedom means doing whatever I want to do—just so I don't get caught.
Evaluation statement: *False. Not getting caught in modern day America is based on pragmatism ("whatever works, is right"). The commands in Scripture are to be obeyed whether we are caught or not.*

❑ Freedom means doing whatever my Christian friends say is okay.
Evaluation statement: *Friends are not the final authority; God's Word is. Christian friends may not know what the Bible says on certain topics.*

❑ Freedom is doing what my conscience allows me to do.
Evaluation statement: *Conscience isn't the final guide. A conscience can be misled. As we mature as Christians, our consciences should become more and more sensitive to what is right and wrong.*

❑ Freedom is doing what I want as long as it's in the privacy of my own home.
Evaluation statement: *False. Privacy is not the final authority in matters of ethics. E.g., I could murder someone in the privacy of my own home and that doesn't make that action right or moral.*

❑ Freedom is being able to do what is right; it's having the inner desire and power inside of me to live within God's boundaries.
Evaluation statement: *God's boundaries are found in the Bible, which does require interpretation. A growing Christian will grow in his desire to please God and the power of the Spirit within Him to obey God's commands from a sincere heart.*

God, My Father (Teacher's Key)

A Study on the Fatherhood of God

Answer the following questions about God as your heavenly Father.

1. Look up the word "father" in a Bible concordance. List four ways—with the verses—that Jesus used the term "Father" when He talked about God in the *Gospel of John*. Which term of "Father" did He use the most?

   a. *"My Father" (John 5:17)*

   b. *"Holy Father" (John 17:11)*

   c. *"The Living Father" (John 6:57)*

   d. *"O, righteous Father" (John 17:25)*

   He used "My Father" the most.

2. Does the New Testament teach that God is the Father of everyone—both believers and non-believers—or just of believers? If God is not exactly the "father" of non-believers, what would He be considered in relationship to them?

   No, the NT teaches that God is the Father of those who become a part of His family by putting their faith in His Son, Jesus Christ. All people are His creatures or creation, however.

3. What three things do you think that a good father should do for his family?

   a.

   b.

   c.

   Answers will vary. Provide financial sustenance, emotional support, and spiritual guidance.

4. Do you see God doing these things for you as your heavenly Father?

   Answers will vary.

5. How does someone become a child of God, and thereby know God as one's heavenly Father? If you don't know Him as your father in this way as yet, would you like to?

   A person becomes God's child by repentance from sin and faith in Jesus Christ.

(cont. ➸)

6. When you talk to God, by what do you address Him the most? God? Jesus? Father? Lord? When you call God your Father, how does it make you feel?

7. List two men whom you think are good fathers. Explain why you think that they are good fathers.

   a. Reason:

   b. Reason:

8. What is the most meaningful part of God being your heavenly Father?

Your Life Goals (Teacher's Key)

Whether you think you know what God has called you to do as a career and/or ministry or not, God will still guide you as you ask Him. Answer the following questions concerning your goals and desires for the future.

1. Make a list of your personal goals and/or desires for the following time frames.

   "In one year, I see myself..."

   "In five years, I see myself..."

   "In ten years, I see myself..."

2. In all of your planning for the future, what have you probably failed to take into consideration?

   My health

3. Do you think that the use of drugs might interfere with your future life goals? Why or why not. Please explain.

   Drugs will make me physically, mentally, emotionally and spiritually incapable of reaching my goals, however noble the goals might be.

4. Write out the following verses. Apply them to your own life in a brief paragraph.

   - *Jeremiah* 29:11

   For I know the thoughts that I think toward you, says the Lord, thoughts of peace and not of evil, to give you a future and a hope. Life applications will differ.

   - *II Corinthians* 5:17

   Therefore, if anyone is in Christ, he is a new creation; old things have passed away; behold, all things have become new. Life applications will differ.*

   - *Matthew* 6:33

   *"...seek first the kingdom of God and His righteousness and all these things** shall be added to you. Therefore, do not worry about tomorrow..." Life applications will differ.*

* "have become" = are constantly becoming new!

** "these things" = the material necessities of life, i.e., food, clothing, and shelter

Vocabulary (Teacher's Key)

Each of the six terms below has been used both correctly and incorrectly in a sentence. Select the line that best describes in context the definition of the term and circle the letter at the start of that sentence. Circle either "A" or "B" for each choice.

Comprehension **Regress** **Hypocrite** **Intellectual** **Humility** **Countenance**

(A.) Susan was able to explain what she had read and so was certain her **comprehension** of the material was adequate.

B. Stan enjoyed the book but felt that the **comprehension** was dry and poorly presented.

A. I decided to attempt to **regress** those topics in my speech to the class.

(B.) After seeing his patient make so much progress, it bothered Dr. Stanton to see his condition **regress**.

A. Stephen wanted to appear that he understood his topic and hoped the audience would see him as a **hypocrite**.

(B.) She knew that by saying one thing and doing the opposite, she would probably be perceived as a **hypocrite**.

(A.) Catrina thoroughly researched and understood her subject and so appeared to have the more **intellectual** of the two presentations.

B. My **intellectual** condition was good but my mind was in a shambles.

A. He was so embarrassed, he finally felt he understood the meaning of **humility**.

(B.) Tiffany realized the project was a big one and had the **humility** to ask for help.

(A.) It was clear from her **countenance** that she was feeling pure joy at that moment.

B. The numbers all added up correctly, so his **countenance** must have been correct.

Questions: The Road to Invention and Discovery (Teacher's Key)

List five famous people from the textbook. Write the question they may have asked that may have helped lead them to their major discovery or invention

Name	Question(s)	Discovery/Invention

Answers on page 271 in Talking About Life's Changes

List three questions that might motivate you to want to create an invention or make a discovery someday.

1. *Answers will vary.*

2. *Answers will vary.*

What Were You Thinking!? (Teacher's Key)

Read the following situations. In the space provided, write what you think each was thinking as they made their choices, what the consequences might be, then explain what you would have done in the same situation and why.

Situation	What were they thinking?	What was the consequence?	What would you have done?
1. After ruining her sister's CD player, Ann blamed it on her younger brother, Timmy. Timmy got punished; Ann got away with it...except Timmy never forgot.	*Ann didn't want to get into trouble. She thought that Timmy couldn't defend himself.*	*Timmy was hurt and bitter toward Ann.*	*I would have taken the blame, fixed the CD player.*
2. Steven was not to trade his basketball cards with friends without his parents' permission. But, he did it anyway. When his parents noticed that one of the more expensive cards had disappeared, Steven told them he lost it. But, his little brother spilled the beans. His parents grounded him for a double length of time for lying as well as disobeying.	*Steven thought it would be fun to trade his cards anyway. He thought he got a "great deal" in the trade.*	*Steven's parents grounded him for a double length of time.*	*I would have obeyed my parents and not have traded any of my cards.*
3. Joe stood by and watched while some of his friends vandalized the school one evening. The police arrived and took them all to the station, where Joe's parents had to bail him out.	*Joe thought that no one would discover them.*	*He was put into jail.*	*I would have not been there at all.*
4. Sara spent the night at a friend's house. With the parents asleep, they snuck out of the house and went to a party. When Sara awoke the next morning, she could not remember many of the things that her friends were telling her that she had done at the party. After vomiting all morning, Sara went home and told her Mom she had the stomach flu.	*Sara might have thought "I'll just try it to see how it tastes."*	*Sara got drunk and did regrettable things.*	*I would not have snuck out to the party.*

Growing in Wisdom (Teacher's Key)

So when they [Joseph and Mary] had performed all things according to the law of the Lord, they returned to Galilee, to their own city, Nazareth. And the Child [Jesus] grew and became strong in spirit, filled with wisdom; and the grace of God was upon Him... And Jesus increased in wisdom and stature and in favor with God and men.

Luke 2:39, 40, 52

1. Look up in a Bible and/or an English dictionary, three definitions of the word "wise" or "wisdom" and record them here.

   Wisdom is: (a) being prudent, discrete, and careful about how one lives; (b) having discernment and insight beyond the surface of things; (c) believing in and preaching Jesus Christ as the ultimate wisdom of God (I Corinthians 1:30)

2. In Scripture, foolishness is the opposite of wisdom. Look up in a Bible and/or an English dictionary, three definitions of the word "foolishness" or "foolish" and record them here.

   Foolishness is: (a) lacking forethought or caution in one's decisions; (b) not showing good judgment; (c) not caring about God or life; being complacent

3. Find three verses in the *Book of Proverbs*, the Bible's book of useful wisdom, that clearly state what is practical wisdom for a person to do. Look up the word "wise" and "wisdom" in a Bible concordance.

   Wisdom means: (a) to have a teachable spirit, Proverbs 1:5, "A wise man will hear and increase learning..."; (b) not to be proud and conceited about your opinions, "Do not be wise in your own eyes; Fear the Lord and depart from evil." Proverbs 3:7; (c) to learn lessons from nature, e.g., about hard work, Proverbs 6:6, "Go to the ant, you sluggard! Consider her ways and be wise..."

4. Find three verses in the *Book of Proverbs*, the Bible's book of useful wisdom, that clearly state what is practical foolishness for a person to do. Look up the word "fool", "foolish" and "foolishness" in a Bible concordance.

   It is foolishness to: (a) hate your mother, Proverbs 15:20, "...a foolish man despises his mother."; (b) waste and/or misspend money, Proverbs 21:20, "...a foolish man squanders it [treasures]"; (c) think that it's not necessary to discipline children, Proverbs 22:15, "Foolishness is bound up in the heart of a child, but the rod of correction will drive it far from him."

(*cont.* ➻)

5. Learn how to apply wisdom to real life situations. Complete the following situation statements with what you think would be the wisest choice(s) for a Christian teen to make:

   a. When a good-looking, non-Christian guy whom she has known all her life asks a Christian girl out on a date, I think the wisest action for her to take would be to...

      not go out with him on a date because the purpose of single dating is to find a marriage partner and the Bible makes it clear that Christians should only marry Christians; it doesn't matter that she has known him all of her life.

   b. When there's going to be an R-rated movie playing at Gary's party that Steve is going to, I think the wisest action for Steve to take would be to...

      Not go to the party or have his parent(s) talk with Gary's parents to see if it really is an R-rated film, and, if so, ask if they could bring Steve later.

   c. When Eddy's older brother, who's a straight "A" student in college, asks his younger brother, Jerry, if he wants to watch him smoke a little pot and look at a *Playboy* magazine, I think the wisest action for Jerry to take would be to...

      Tell his brother that he's not interested in either pot or porn and not to bother asking him again.

6. Look up the phrase "blind spot" in an English dictionary or talk to a trusted adult as to the meaning of the phrase and record it here. (Record the meaning that applies to people's character rather than to the retina of the eye.) What is the one main area in life in which you feel you may have a "blind spot"; the area of weakness in your life for which you need the most wisdom? How might you provide more wisdom for yourself in that area?

   a. Definition of a blind spot:*A "blind spot" is an area or subject about which one is uninformed, prejudiced, or unappreciative.*

   b. One of your personal blind spots: *Answers will vary.*

   c. How you're going to get more wisdom for this blind spot:*Answers will vary.*

The Importance of Prayer (Teacher's Key)

BIBLE STUDY

1. Look up the words "pray" and "prayer" in a Bible dictionary and/or an English dictionary. Record three definitions here.

   a. *Prayer is talking with God.*

   b. *Prayer is listening to God.*

   c. *Prayer is communing with God in one's heart and feeling His presence.*

2. Read all of *Matthew* 7:7-11. Verse 11 says, "If you then, being evil, know how to give good gifts to your children, how much more will your Father who is in heaven give good things to those who ask Him." From these verses, what can you learn about the attitude of the Father toward His children?

   God is very generous and He wants to bless His children.

   How could this give you confidence in your prayers?

   God's generosity can give us more confidence in our prayers because we know that He wants to answer them.

3. Read all of *Luke* 11:5-10. Verse 10 says, "For everyone who asks [keeps on asking] receives, and he who seeks [keeps on seeking] finds, and to him who knocks [keeps on knocking], it will be opened." To what kind of prayer does God respond?

   persistent prayer

4. Read all of *Luke* 18:10-14. Verse 14 says, "...for everyone who exalts himself will be abased and he who humbles himself will be exalted." From this story, what two character qualities are required for God to answer prayer?

   a. *humility*

   b. *repentance*

5. Read *Matthew* 5:20-24. Verse 24 says, "First be reconciled to your brother, and then come and offer your gift." What kind of attitude toward others does God require for us to have before He will hear our prayers?

   A forgiving attitude

6. Read *Luke* 5:16, "So He Himself [Jesus] often withdrew into the wilderness and prayed." Why do you think that Jesus often withdrew from the people and His busy ministry schedule in order to pray? What might this teach you about your conversations with God?

   Jesus needed to be alone so that He could focus on the Father and hear His voice. His solitude for prayer teaches us that we need to find a place alone to be able to have quality time with God.

(*cont.* ➸)

7. Explain how the following verses teach us more about how to get our prayers answered:

   - Simplicity and sincerity, *Matthew* 6:5

     Prayer doesn't need to be fancy, memorized, long, or formal.

   - Faith, *Mark* 9:23

     We need to have confidence that the Father wants to bless us. But, we should pray that His will is done and not demand that our desires are answered because He alone knows the "big picture."

"So, What's the Big Deal?" (Teacher's Key)

A Study on Hypocrisy

1. Look up "hypocrisy" in a dictionary. What is its definition?

   The false profession of desirable or publicly approved qualities, beliefs, or feelings, especially a pretense of having virtues, moral principles, or religious beliefs that one does not really possess.

2. A person who practices hypocrisy is called *a hypocrite* or *hypocritical*.

3. Look up the word "deceive" in a dictionary. What is its definition?

   To mislead by a false appearance or statement; to trick

4. How is hypocrisy like deceit?

   A person who is "acting" is purposefully misleading others.

5. Look in a thesaurus and list three other words used for a hypocrite.

   deceiver, fraud, pretender, faker

6. Look up the following references. Write down the instance of hypocrisy, who the hypocrite(s) was, and the reason Jesus criticized them.

   - *Matthew* 26:25

     a. Instance: *the betrayal of Jesus*

     b. Hypocrite(s): *Judas*

     c. Reason: *Judas pretended to be loyal to Jesus, but sold Him out for money.*

   - *Matthew* 15:1-9

     a. Instance: *discussion of Jewish traditions*

     b. Hypocrite(s): *the scribes, Pharisees, the Jewish people*

     c. Reason: *The Jews missed the main point in the laws.*

   - *Matthew* 22:18

     a. Instance: *discussing the payment of taxes*

     b. Hypocrite(s): *the Pharisees and the Herodians*

     c. Reason: *These men had impure motives in their asking of their questions. They wanted him to offend the Jews and/or the Romans.*

(*cont.* ➻)

- *John* 8:1-11

  a. Instance: *A woman caught in adultery*

  b. Hypocrite(s): *scribes and Pharisees*

  c. Reason: *All were sinners, not just the woman.*

- *Luke* 13:10-17

  a. Instance: *Christ healing the crippled woman on the Sabbath day*

  b. Hypocrite(s): *the Jews and the ruler of the synagogue*

  c. Reason: *They missed the main point of the Sabbath. It was fine to do good to people. They were already doing good to their animals, which were their livelihood.*

7. Write out *James* 3:17.

But the wisdom that is from above is first pure, then peaceable, gentle, willing to yield, full of mercy and good fruits, without partiality and without hypocrisy.

Student Text Chapter Review Answer Keys

(These are the answers to the Chapter Reviews that occur at the end of each chapter in the student text.)

Chapter 1 Review Answers

Defining the Terms

(If the following terms are not clearly defined in this chapter, use the definition from a dictionary.)

Temptation: something that allures or draws someone especially to evil

Consequences: the effect, outcome or result of something

Influence: the power of persons or things to produce effects on others

Habit: a pattern of behavior established from repetition

Deception: the act of misleading by false appearance or statement, to trick

Soul: a person's mind, will, and emotions

Total Health: physical, mental, social and spiritual well-being

Recalling the Facts

1. Satan began to question Eve about what God really had said. He wanted to isolate her from Adam and from God. He tried to trick her by lying to her about God's intentions. He brought doubt into her mind.
2. Their eyes were opened to good and evil. They recognized they were naked. Deception brought fear and separation from God. Adam and Eve hid from God and felt afraid of God. They did not feel they could tell Him what they had done.
3. Adam and Eve's "forbidden fruit" was the tree in the middle of the garden. It was God's commandment to them not to eat from it. To us, it's something that God wants us to stay away from.
4. The Tree of Life means to be dependent upon God, knowing your need for others, to be involved, talking with safe adults, telling the truth and being open and transparent about your thoughts and feelings. The Tree of Death leads you to be independent from God, seeing no need for others, being isolated, not talking with safe adults, covering up, being dishonest and being closed and afraid to share thoughts and feelings.
5. God called for them and sought them out.
6. Physically: disease, decay, death, and pain in childbirth. Adam would have to work hard in manual labor and struggle for food.

   Mentally: Mankind would struggle with the animals. Experience mental and emotional stress from fear of bad climate and dangerous beasts.

   Socially: Severe conflict between human beings. Jealousy, hatred, violence.

   Spiritually: The spirit of mankind, which was once in close union with God, would now be separated because of sin. Feelings of loneliness and isolation.

Applying the Truth

1. Do not be wise in your own eyes, don't be influenced by others or "go along" with an evil crowd of people who would want you to do wrong. Flee evil, don't hang around just to "check things out".
2. Pressure to disobey your parents, temptation to give into peer pressure of immorality, gossip, drinking alcohol, trying drugs and tobacco. A desire to do things that you know will not be pleasing to God.
3. Personal reflection; the answer is subjective. Encourage discussion of the importance of talking to a safe, Christian adult they can trust. Positive choice: a person who wants them to please the Lord, the Bible, and their parents. Negative choice: a person who does not care about what is right or wrong; does not support them by praying for or with them; is not a strong, growing Christian.
4. Possible answers may include: choice of friends, study habits in school, food choices, decision to try tobacco, drugs, or alcohol, decision to get involved with the opposite sex, the decision to improve their communication with their parent(s).

Chapter 2 Review Answers

Defining the Terms

Healthy: a state of physical, mental, social and spiritual wellbeing

Cells: the basic building blocks of the body from which all larger parts are formed

Tissues: similar cells organized into specialized groups to carry out particular functions

Arteriosclerosis: hardening of the arteries

Organ: two or more tissues grouped together to perform a singular function

Arteries: carry oxygenated blood away from the heart

Veins: carry blood that lacks oxygen (deoxygenated blood) back to the heart

Capillaries: the smallest blood vessels

Plasma: the liquid portion of the blood

Red blood cells: the portion of the blood that carries oxygen

White blood cells: the portion of the blood that fights germs, viruses, and diseases

Platelets: the portion of the blood that helps the blood to clot

Blood pressure: the force that your blood puts on the inside walls of your blood vessels

Stroke: when the flow of blood to one part of the brain is severely restricted or cut off

Pharynx: the throat

Trachea: carries air to the lungs

Esophagus: a passageway that carries food to the stomach

Epiglottis: a small flap of skin that prevents food from entering the trachea

Lungs: large, soft cone-shaped organs used for breathing

Diaphragm: a large muscle that separates the chest from the abdomen

Skeletal muscles: muscles that cause the body to move

Smooth muscles: muscles found in the digestive system and blood vessels which provide movement within the body

Cardiac muscle: the heart muscle

Digestion: the process by which food is broken down and made useful for the body

Alimentary canal: a long muscular tube that extends from the mouth to the anus

Large intestine: the cecum, colon, rectum, and anal canal; moves waste through the body

Small intestine: where most of the digestion and absorption of nutrients occurs

Kidneys: two bean-shaped organs that cleanse the blood of impurities and send it back to the bloodstream

Homeostasis: a balanced, stable internal environment inside the body

Hormones: chemicals released by the glands of the endocrine system; often called "chemical messengers"

Pituitary gland: located in the brain, the master gland releasing the growth hormone

Thyroid gland: hormones released from the thyroid control how fast the body metabolizes (uses) food for energy

Adrenal glands: release hormones in response to certain types of stress; responsible for the "fight-or-flight" response

Ovaries: the glands of the female reproductive system, located inside the female body; gradually release hormones responsible for female sex characteristics

Testes: the glands of the male reproductive system, located outside the male body; gradually release hormones responsible for male sex characteristics

Recalling the Facts

1. Each individual cell is living, moving, sensing, breathing, reproducing, growing, eliminating, eating/drinking.
2. Epithelial tissues: cover all body surfaces inside and out

   Connective tissues: bind structures together providing support and protection

   Muscle tissues: provide movement

   Nerve tissues: receive and transmit impulses to various parts of the body
3. The circulatory system is like a major transportation system. It transports fuel to the body, carries wastes to the liver and kidneys, sends cells to fight disease, and transports hormones throughout the body.
4. You can choose to hold your breath, but sooner or later your body's need for oxygen will overcome your own ability to resist, and you will gasp for air.
5. Support, protection, manufacture, storage
6. Skeletal muscles work in pairs. While one muscle contracts (shortens) the other extends (lengthens). A baseball player swings a bat (triceps and biceps muscles). Another pair would be the quad and the hamstring of the thigh, or the back and stomach muscles.
7. The purpose of the excretory system is to provide ways for waste to be removed from the body. Even if a car owner tuned his engine and put fresh oil into it daily, if the exhaust system was not working, there would be something wrong with the car. What would happen to your car if you put a potato in the exhaust pipe? Liken this to constipation!

Applying the Truth

1. Helped: All systems are helped in some way, but the circulatory, cardiovascular, respiratory, muscular, skeletal, digestive and excretory systems are most directly affected. More efficient use of oxygen, strengthens the heart muscle, increases oxygen to the blood, strengthens the bones and muscles for protection and longevity, improves digestion and absorption of nutrients, and improves the ability of the elimination of wastes.
2. Every body system is hurt by poor nutrition; however, the circulatory, cardiovascular, digestive, and excretory systems are more directly affected. Poor diet causes hardening of the arteries, lowers ability to fight off diseases, makes the heart work harder than normal, slows down the digestive system, and makes the excretory system become less efficient. Teens should consider less

junk food that is high in salt, fat and sugar. Diet soda pop with its dangerous chemicals as well as regular soda pop that is high in sugar, should be limited in their diets. Eat more fresh vegetables and fruit to help these systems.

3. • The vomiting reflex: saves us from poisons
   • Fertilization of a single cell
   • The miles of nerves that run through the body
   • The incredible numbers of blood cells constantly flowing through the body
   • The body's ability to maintain a balanced internal environment despite the outside temperature, stress, etc.
   • The difference between the male and female bone structure for specific purpose: for example, the female pelvis created for delivery of children

Chapter 3 Review Answers

Defining the Terms

Balanced diet: making food choices that include a wide variety from all that God has given to us in nature

Calorie: a unit of heat that your body uses for activity

Empty calories: those foods that don't have any nutritive value

Nutrients: substances in foods that your body needs (proteins, carbohydrates, fats, vitamins, minerals and water)

Proteins: a string of amino acids used by the body to build new cells and tissues

Essential amino acids: eight amino acids that your body does not produce naturally and must get from the foods you eat

Vegetarian diet: a diet that typically excludes animal products

Carbohydrates: Sugars and starches that the body uses for energy

Fats: concentrated sources of energy that can provide twice as much energy than carbohydrates

Saturated fat: these fats are solid at room temperature which tend to increase blood cholesterol

Cholesterol: a fatty substance in the blood which increases the risk of heart disease

Unsaturated fats: usually liquid at room temperature and don't tend to raise blood cholesterol

Vitamins: organic substances the body needs in small amounts

RDA: Recommended Daily Allowance

Water-soluble: vitamins that dissolve in water and can pass through the body

Fat-soluble: vitamins that don't dissolve in water and can be stored in the body

Minerals: inorganic substances that are essential for the body

Metabolic rate: the speed at which your body burns calories

Diet: all the foods you choose to eat on a regular basis

Overweight: weighing more than the desired weight for age, sex, height and frame size

Obese: weighing more than 20% over ideal weight

Anorexia: self-induced starvation

Bulimia: a pattern of "binging" and "purging"

Chronic overeating: the habit of eating more food than your body needs

Recalling the Facts

1. The Food Pyramid recommends 6-11 servings of whole grains and high-fiber foods. Next, 2-4 servings of fruit and 3-5 of vegetables. The dairy section suggests 2-3 servings and the protein group 2-3 as well. Fats and sugars should be minimal. If I were to adjust the Food Pyramid, I would have the base category be filled with fresh fruits and vegetables and then the next group be the whole grains.
2. Saturated fats are solid at room temperature and tend to raise blood cholesterol. Unsaturated fats are liquid at room temperature and do not tend to raise blood cholesterol. Saturated fats are the most dangerous because they increase the chance of heart disease and other diseases. Butter is a saturated fat and vegetable oil is an unsaturated fat.
3. Water is the most common nutrient in your body. Without water, you would die. Your body uses water for cleansing of waste and toxins, lubricating joints, transporting nutrients, regulating body temperature, losing weight, and digesting food.
4. A food journal shows eating patterns. How much and what kind of food you eat at various times of the day. Sometimes you may eat and not know why or remember how much ("How many cookies did I just eat?"). You can make changes in your diet after evaluating "weak" times during the day when you may have the tendency to overeat or eat the wrong kinds of food.
5. Answers may vary, but some ideas include: Eat less sugar and sodium, drink more water, increase my dietary fiber, try to maintain my ideal weight without doing fad diets, eat a variety of foods and eat less saturated fat.
6. Fad diets are dangerous because usually they make promises that are unhealthy for your body. Many diet drinks have tons of sugar and lack the vi-

tal nutrients necessary to keep your body functioning (for example, fiber needed for regular bowel movements). Going on a diet makes you think of the short-term because it is an "on" and "off" decision rather than a lifestyle change.

Applying the Truth

1. A pizza contains carbohydrates, vegetables, and protein. A healthy pizza order would include low-fat cheeses and a whole-wheat crust, topped with lots of vegetables.
2. Keys to a great food journal are: (1) Be honest and write down everything I eat. (2) Be exact in writing down what I eat. (3) Be accountable to someone. (4) Fill in the comment section to help me understand why and when I eat certain foods. These will be hard because I must take extra time actually to think about what I am eating and how much. Then I have to be honest and share my food choices with another person—this can be embarrassing, especially if I don't choose the right person.
3. Answers may vary based on a person's previous knowledge of the Food Pyramid. Some answers may include: the number of servings for the bread, cereal group, or the fact that fruits and vegetables were not on the bottom. Each student may make dietary changes under the Food Pyramid based on their current eating habits.
4. Package labeling can be misleading because: the fancy packaging, the claims for being "fat-free" or "lite". Serving sizes can be misleading because they may be unusually small for the food product. Labels may also leave out specific amounts of ingredients such as hydrogenated oils and tropical oils.
5. Imagine you have a friend who seems to have poor eating habits and you are very concerned. How might you determine if they have a problem with anorexia or bulimia? What might you say and/or do to help your friend?

   Watch your friend closely for signs of self-starvation, overexercising, using the bathroom after meals (vomiting or purging), or an extreme concern about watching her weight. If you have a good relationship with the individual and his/her family, you could try to talk with the parent(s) about your concern without her knowing. Ask her if she feels she is having a problem and wants your support and help. Do not criticize or tease her about her body or eating habits. Suggest a good book for you or your friend to read such as: *Walking the Thin Line: Anorexia and Bulimia, the Battle Can Be Won* by Pam Vredevelt; *The Monster Within: Overcoming Bulimia*; *The Courage to Go On*; or *Food for the Hungry Heart* by Cynthia Rowland McClure.

Chapter 4 Review Answers

Defining the Terms

Fitness: the ability of your mind and body to work together to their highest possible level

Cardiovascular fitness: the condition of the heart

Atrophy: occurs when a long period of time lapses between workouts and the muscles decrease in size and strength

Aerobic: when your muscles demand more oxygen than normal during an activity

Anaerobic: short bursts of activity without the use of much oxygen

Muscular fitness: the measurement of your muscle strength and muscle endurance

Flexibility: the ability to move your joints and muscles through a full range of motion

Body composition: the relationship between your fat and lean (muscle) body weight

Lifetime sports: activities that a person can participate in throughout a lifetime

Recalling the Facts

1. List of 16 is on page 70 of student text.
2. Without strong heart, lungs, and blood vessels working together to supply oxygenated blood to the whole body, without strong cardiovascular fitness, it would not matter how much weight you could lift if you died from a heart attack!
3. Aerobic exercise is activity that requires oxygen to perform. Swimming, running, and playing basketball are examples of aerobic exercise. It is important to include aerobic exercise in your life because it improves your cardiovascular fitness. Anaerobic exercise is activity that does not require much oxygen to perform. Anaerobic exercise is important for muscular strength and coordination development. Weightlifting, sprinting, and golf are examples of anaerobic activity.
4. A person should listen to his/her body because pain is the signal that something is wrong. There may be slight pain in stretching or exercising but you should never push past the point of pain. The nerve reflex

protects your muscle by sending the pain signal. When you stretch too far, you are tightening the very muscles you are trying to loosen.

5. The warm-up prepares your muscles for activity. The body temperature must rise enough to increase the body temperature. Stretching should occur after the body is warm. A warm-down is important because the muscles need to release the build-up of lactic acid from the workout, and will decrease the muscle soreness, cramping, nausea or lightheadedness that can occur after a workout. Both a proper warm-up and warm-down help prevent injuries.

Applying the Truth

1. Regular aerobic exercise helps control a person's weight because of the extra calories that are burned through activity. Increase in muscle mass also helps because muscles burn more calories than fat. Teenagers can increase their exercise by joining an athletic team, riding their bike to school or other locations, getting involved with yard work or playing a non-competitive sport with friends.
2. An accidental workout means to increase in your activity level when you don't even know you are doing it. It is making exercise and movement a fun and enjoyable part of your daily life, e.g., riding horses, bike riding, skateboarding, jump rope, etc.
3. Comparing with your peers concerning appearance and skill. Comparing is one of the greatest enemies to your mind because it will either make you feel superior to others who aren't as good as you, or make you feel inferior to others who are better than you. God never intended for you to compare yourself with others. God only expects you to do your best and become the finest person you can become with the resources He's given to you.

Chapter 5 Review Answers

Defining the Terms

Homeostasis: a balanced, stable internal environment in the body

Disease: any condition that negatively affects the healthy and normal functioning of your mind or body

Infectious disease: caused by germs that spread from one person to another

Noninfectious disease: caused by heredity, the environment, and a person's lifestyle

Germs or Pathogens: tiny particles that may be plant or animal that cause disease

Symptoms: reactions from your body (stuffy nose, sore throat), that indicate that it is trying to fight an intruder, an infection. Your body redirects its energy to fight the germ.

Viruses: smaller than bacteria and attack individual cells. They are responsible for the common cold, chicken pox, measles, and AIDS.

Bacteria: single-celled tiny organisms that attack your body. Strep throat, pneumonia, and some STD's are caused by bacteria.

Resident Bacteria: "friendly" bacteria that your body needs

Antibodies: protein molecules produced by your white blood cells to fight off germs

Lymphocytes: white blood cells that fight off germs

Vaccine: weakened or destroyed cells of a particular germ that are injected into a person to produce enough antibodies to keep a person from contracting the disease

STD: sexually transmitted disease(s) (venereal disease) that pass from one person to another through sexual contact

Convictions: a person's strong belief on a particular issue

AIDS: Acquired Immunodeficiency Syndrome

HIV: Human Immunodeficiency Virus

Cancer: a disease which occurs when abnormal cells grow out of control

Tumor: masses of abnormal cells

Carcinogen: any natural or man-made substance that tends to produce cancer

Congenital: occurring at birth

Insulin: a hormone produced by the pancreas to control how the body uses sugar

Diabetes type I: insulin-dependent where the pancreas produces little or no insulin

Diabetes type II: non-insulin dependent where the pancreas does not produce enough insulin to meet the body's needs or the body can't use it correctly

Recalling the Facts

1. The body works very hard to maintain a stable and balanced internal environment so that each system functions efficiently for maximum health.
2. Germs can be spread in four ways: contact with an airborne germ, contact with an infected person, contact with infected animals, and contact with objects that an infected person has handled. From the time you become infected to the time you develop symptoms is

called the incubation period, during which you are highly contagious.

3. Your body has both good (resident) bacteria and bad (illness-causing) bacteria. The body needs good bacteria to fight off the germs that invade the body. Antibiotics kill both the good and bad bacteria so you need to replace the good bacteria in your body.
4. Most germs are carried through contact with an infected person or infected item. Keeping your hands washed is the best form of defense for you against germs.
5. The skin is the first line of defense. The mucous membranes in your mouth, nose, and throat protect you from invading germs. The hairs inside your nose help keep small particles out. If germs have invaded your body, your white blood cells begin to produce special proteins called antibodies to fight the germs. When an individual cell is invaded by a germ, the body produces interferon to inform the other cells to fight the germ. If the virus cannot enter the other cells, then the infection has been stopped. A fever also works to burn off an invader.
6. Sexual abstinence
7. • Genetic make-up (heredity)
   • Lifestyle habits
   • Environmental factors
   • Occupational hazards
   • Your body's reaction to a virus

   A person can directly control lifestyle, some elements of the environment, and their occupational choice. Heredity and your body's reaction to a virus (that is if you are keeping yourself as healthy as possible) are out of your direct control.
8. • Discover if you have any heart disease in your family.
   • Have a healthy lifestyle that includes a diet of fresh fruits and vegetables, and limit the fats and salt.
   • Exercise regularly to keep your heart fit and to decrease the effects of stress.

Applying the Truth

1. Even though Kristen was young when she got sick, she had a normal reaction to such bad news. Her attitude about living life to its fullest was positive even in the worst circumstances. God is sovereign in all His ways even though we don't always understand why things happen.
2. "Listen to your body" means to pay special attention to the symptoms you feel and your changing health. Maybe certain foods upset your stomach or you don't do well when you do not get enough sleep. You can change some health habits as you learn to listen to your body.
3. The Word of God, faith in God's power, faith in God's control
4. Lifestyle includes: food choices (consumption of alcohol, drugs, coffee, soda pop, processed foods), amount of exercise, involvement with the opposite sex.
5. It is important to know what you believe and why you believe it before you find yourself in a compromising situation. Often people do things they will regret because they have not developed strong convictions before a temptation faces them.

Chapter 6 Review Answers

Defining the Terms

Mature: showing good development and growth: physically, mentally, emotionally, socially and spiritually

Confident: no feelings of inferiority

Personal identity: to know who you are in Christ

Jealousy: feeling of resentment against another for having a success or talent that you want to have

Pride: to think yourself better than you really are; an "I don't need anyone"/"I'm better than others" attitude

Character: what you are on the inside, what you do when no one is watching

Self-esteem: the way you feel about yourself

Recalling the Facts

1. • *Physical:* possible acne, increase in height and weight, needing to shower more often
   • *Mental (emotional):* increased stress, feelings of independence, inability to "relate" to adults, and that general feeling that "no one understands"
   • *Social:* possible increased tension at home, attraction to the opposite sex, increased peer pressure, and the desire for more freedom
   • *Spiritual:* an overall sense "I want to get closer to God but I don't know how", or other questions about God's role in your own life
2. A teen experiences things so intensely because of all the changes taking place in his/her body: physical changes, emotional frustrations, social

pressures, and spiritual concerns.

3. First, identify your worries, starting with the greatest one. After you realize what the greatest source of worry is right now, share it with God. As you are talking with God, take the time just to listen to what He says to you in your mind and in your heart. He will give you a sense of peace about your concern. Next, talk to someone you can trust, preferably an adult.
4. God wants to mold you into the likeness of Jesus Christ—to become more like Him!

Applying the Truth

1. When a potter throws a pot, the clay must be of good quality (the clay represents your life). Each change to the piece brings it closer to what the artist (God) wants the pot to become. God never makes mistakes, and does not give up on a piece of clay! But the clay must cooperate and be pliable. The purpose for the vessel has been determined before the potter begins his work on the piece. Once the artist believes the vessel needs strengthening or testing, it will go into the fire (difficult times for a Christian). Depending upon the purpose for the piece, the clay may have to experience the intense heat of the fire over and over again. But every time, if the clay does not crack under the pressure, it comes out stronger, ready for use.
2. Sometimes bad things happen to Christians, just like non-Christians. Many times, you don't understand why things happen. There is no easy answer for this, but God has a unique way of causing good to come from bad. I know it is hard right now, but if you turn to God and share your true feelings, He will help you through this time.
3. Comparison and jealousy ruin relationships. They put a big wedge between you and the other person. They also affect your thoughts about yourself. Possibly worst of all, they can lead you into pride to think that you are better than others. If you have a problem with jealousy, talk to God about the way you feel and ask Him to help you overcome comparison and be grateful for all that He has done for you.
4. Answers may vary but the general theme for each illustration should include:
   - The Faithful Servant: Increase Your Personal Responsibilities. "He who is faithful in little will be faithful in much."
   - Samuel: Focus on What Really Matters. "Man looks on the outward, but God looks at the heart."
   - King David: Grow in Openness to God. "My God, my God, why have you forsaken me?"
   - Judas: Avoid Secrecy and Isolation. Judas "went out and it was night."
   - Joseph: Learn How to Forgive Those Who Hurt You. "You meant it for evil, but God meant it for good."
   - Peter: Stand-Alone Courage. "But Peter...raised his voice and said to them..."

Chapter 7 Review Answers

Defining the Terms

Distract: to divide the mind

Self-control: being able to restrain your words or behaviors that might hurt you or someone else

Boundary: an invisible line that separates you from everyone and everything else; like a fence with a gate that you control between you and the outside world

Goal: an achievement toward which you work; your personal aim, purpose, or end in doing or not doing something

Short-term goal: something that you make specific plans to accomplish within a relatively brief period of time

Long-term goal: something that you make specific plans to get done over a relatively long period of time

Recalling the Facts

1. Society values having a lot of money, fame, intelligence, and good looks.

   God values inner character qualities like self-control, love, kindness, obedience, respect, and wisdom.
2. 1) Make wise choices
   2) Stay mentally focused
   3) Gain self-control
   4) Develop appropriate boundaries
   5) Set realistic goals
   6) Become a lifelong learner
   7) Stay motivated
3. • Learn from others' experiences
   • Get input from mature adults you trust
   • Take time to think about your decisions
   • Pray for wisdom

Applying the Truth

1. • Homework: Turn off the TV and the music. Reward yourself when you reach small goals. Use a student calendar to stay organized. Study

in the library instead of at home. Don't take any phone calls until after you have completed your work.

- Chores around the house: Give yourself a time limit and pace yourself. Don't allow yourself to do anything 'fun' until your chores are done.
- Finishing projects that you start: Set small goals for the project so it does not seem so overwhelming. Learn not to procrastinate. Work with another person. Be accountable to someone about your schedule.
- Music lessons: Don't wait until you "feel" like practicing. Set the same time everyday to practice. Make it a part of your daily routine.

2. A boundary is an invisible barrier between you and the outside world. It helps to prevent you from hurting yourself physically or emotionally by making unwise choices that are outside your boundary. They stop you from hurting others feelings and they give you a way of protecting yourself by being able confidently to say "No".
3. If you were to cheat on a math test it would be a sin, but if you got an answer wrong on your math test because you forgot how to do the problem or did not understand, then it is a mistake but not a sin. A sin is a moral or spiritual transgression, contradictory to God's nature and His laws. A mistake, like missing a math problem, is not a sin (although you probably could have studied a little bit more!) Even though all sins are mistakes, all mistakes are not sins. If you sinned, repent and He will forgive you (*I John* 1:9). If you made a mistake that wasn't a sin, learn to accept your weaknesses; live and learn.
4. Satan wants you to feel depressed, fearful and unmotivated to change. This keeps you away from God and others. Satan wants you to harden your heart but God wants you to have a heart that is willing to change. When Satan tries to keep you away from God and others who might help you, God wants you to go to Him and others immediately and not to wait. God wants to help you learn from your mistakes and cause good to come from them.

Chapter 8 Review Answers

Defining the Terms

Social health: your ability to get along with different kinds of people

Friendship: a social connection in which people willingly share common interests or activities

Relationship: a tie with people by blood, marriage, work, or social role

Substitutions: replacing one person or thing with another

Artificial relationships: bonding with someone or something that doesn't really exist as an actual living person in real life

Communication: the act of expressing thoughts, feelings, information, or beliefs easily or effectively through speech, writing, media, or signs

Verbal communication: sharing a message through words or talking

Nonverbal communication: sharing a message without talking such as body language, hand motions, or facial expressions

A Wall: a barrier between people that hinders their communication

Infatuation: feeling temporary strong emotional attraction to a person of the opposite sex

Positive peer pressure: what you feel when others encourage you to do something that is good for you or others

Negative peer pressure: what you feel when others encourage you to do something that is harmful for you or others

Respect: esteem, admiration, acceptance, or courtesy; not intruding upon or interfering with another person's rights

Disrespect: lack of courtesy, rude, insulting, sarcastic, or sassy

Reputation: what people think of you

Revenge: wanting to get even with someone

Forgive: release all of your desire to punish or get even with those who have hurt or offended you

Empathy: when you really feel for a person who is hurt because you've experienced the same hurt

Recalling the Facts

1. A computer program or game, a Hollywood actor or actress, a star athlete or the lives of those on a soap opera or sitcom can become artificial relationships for some teens. This is dangerous because it can promote isolation and a lack of accountability with others.
2. Jonathan and David (*I Samuel* 18:1-4) had a unique friendship because they shared deeply and openly with one another. They sacrificed for the good of the other person.
3. Communicating is expressing thoughts, feelings and information effectively. To do this, a person must learn to listen and understand the other person rather than just "talk" about his/her own opinions.

4. 1) Realize that first impressions can be misleading.
   2) Choose the right time and place.
   3) Know what your true feelings are—and stick to them.
   4) Avoid yelling, screaming, and name-calling.
   5) Be an active and sensitive listener.
   6) Be quick to apologize.
   7) Accept the person even if you reject the idea.
   8) Recognize walls in yourself and others.
   9) Use "I" statements instead of "You" statements.
   10) Describe the present situation only. Avoid statements that use the words "never" and "always".
   11) Accept the fact that some conflicts will take time to be resolved.
   12) Put yourself in the other person's place.
5. • Define what the purpose is for 'single dating'.
   • Know your level of maturity.
   • Know your parent's dating standards for you.
6. Develop good communication skills with your parents and mature, safe adults. When you invest in healthy friendships, you surround yourself with the positive influence of good friends. As a result, negative peer pressure won't affect you as much.

Applying the Truth

1. The words that you use to talk with others come from your heart and your mind. They include words you hear most of the time, from what kinds of music you listen to, and what kind of books you read. If you fill your mind and heart with nonsense words, nonsense words will be what you speak. But if you fill your mind and heart with godly words and thoughts, then these words will be communicated through your speech. Words can never be "taken back" and can hurt another person's feelings.
2. When a teen shows favoritism only to those who look good, wear designer clothes, have money, are intelligent, have athletic ability, or have a cool car, they are showing partiality. God wants us to show unconditional respect to all people, Christian and non-Christian. God made each person in His image and for His own special purpose.
3. Gossips don't have many friends except for others who gossip. They can't keep their friends very long because they don't respect other people's private matters. Ask God to help you overcome the temptation to gossip. The next time you are around friends, practice saying something nice about a person who is not with you and see what the response is in the group. Speaking positively about others is part of becoming more like Christ.

Chapter 9 Review Answers

Defining the Terms

Epidermis: the outer layer of skin

Dermis: the middle layer of skin

Subcutaneous layer: the deepest layer of skin

Acne: occurs when the pores of your skin become clogged with oil

Sebum: an oily substance that eventually clogs the pores of your skin

Blackhead: a pore that's plugged with oil—but is exposed to the air

Whitehead: a type of acne that is created when oil becomes trapped inside a pore

Pimple: a clogged pore that has become infected and filled with pus. Pimples are the most serious type of acne.

Dermatologist: a doctor who treats skin disorders

Follicle: The roots of your hair are secured in these small pockets.

Dandruff: a condition in which the outer layer of skin on the scalp flakes off

Head lice: insects that live in the hair and look very similar to dandruff

Keratin: a hard substance that gives nails their strength

Cuticle: surrounds the nail and is made of a nonliving skin. The cuticle protects the base of the nail from germs and bacteria.

Ingrown toenail: a nail that pushes into the skin on the side of your toe

Masticate: chew thoroughly

Periodontium: the name of the bone, tissue, and gum that support your teeth

Cavity: when bacteria combines with sugary foods and forms an acid

Plaque: a grainy, sticky coating that is constantly forming on your teeth

Tartar: a substance that hardens on your teeth

Gingivitis: is a gum disease caused by a build-up of plaque and tarter on your teeth

Periodontal disease: more advanced gum disease

Malocclusion: when your upper and lower teeth don't line up properly

Orthodontics: braces can treat severe irregularities of the teeth

Halitosis: bad breath

Farsightedness: a condition where a person has difficulty seeing things that are close

Nearsightedness: a condition where a person has difficulty seeing things that are far away

Astigmatism: a condition in which a person's vision is distorted due to the irregular shape of the cornea or lens

Pink eye: a very contagious condition caused by a bacterial infection

Sty: when one of the small glands in your eyelid gets infected and swollen. It may look like a pimple.

Recalling the Facts

1. • Being clean and attractive will definitely enhance your looks, but try not to fall into the trap of always wanting to look good for other people.
   - Taking care of yourself makes you feel good about yourself.
   - Using good personal hygiene shows respect, not only to others, but also to yourself.
   - Practicing good hygiene daily will boost your confidence in social situations and positively affect your relationship with others.
2. The worst time to be in the sun is between 10:00AM and 3:00PM. The sun is too intense for your skin and can cause a burn.
3. Do
   - Wash with a facial cleanser and warm water twice a day.
   - Dry your skin carefully with a clean towel. Don't scrub the area.
   - Use a mild cleanser suited to your skin type (to help control the excess oil).
   - Get plenty of rest.
   - Exercise regularly.
   - Eat fresh whole foods.
   - Drink more than eight glasses of purified water daily.
   - Wear oil-free make-up.
   - If your condition is serious, see a dermatologist (a doctor who treats skin disorders).
   - Understand that acne will eventually go away.

   Don't
   - Squeeze or pick at your acne. This can cause infection and scarring.
   - Use heavy creams or moisturizers on the affected areas.
   - Touch your face with your hands or fingers. This can place more oil and dirt on your face.
   - Let acne get you depressed or prevent you from having fun!
4. • First, try to stay calm. If you've ever changed your hairstyle—or got a 'fad' cut—then you know how it can affect your whole outlook on life. One good line to tell yourself after you get your hair cut is, "It'll always grow back!"
   - Second, there are different types of hair. It's true that different hair types need different shampoos, conditioners, and cuts to maximize their style, but try not to stop there. Look at the shape of your head and face to help to determine what kind of style is right for you.
   - Third, hairstyles change as often as clothing styles. Try not to pick the "in" cut if it's not the best for you. Find something that makes you feel good and confident about yourself and stick with it. Another good question to keep in mind about any new hairstyle is, "Is this style really practical for me?" If you have a hard time getting up in the morning, for example, try to stay away from a hairstyle that demands major styling time.
5. • Brush your teeth after each meal.
   - Brush your tongue.
   - Change your toothbrush.
   - Floss at least once a day.
   - Use fluoride.
   - Eat healthfully.
   - Visit your dentist twice a year.
6. In the center of the iris is the pupil.
7. The most common form of ear trouble is an ear infection. A viral or bacterial infection of the nose, throat, or Eustachian tubes can cause intense ear pain. Unlike a middle-ear infection, swimmer's ear occurs in the outer ear.
8. When sitting down, try always to have your seat and lower back pushed back up against the back of the chair. This will help to prevent undue stress on your lower back muscles and prevent lower back pain. Imagine a string with a helium balloon connected to the crown (the very highest part) of your head. Pretend the balloon is pulling straight upward. Your chin should go down and your neck come back into proper alignment with your shoulders. If you still have posture problems, imagine that same string and balloon on the front of your chest pulling your chest up and out.
9. • Take special note of how you feel when you bite your nails. Do you feel bored, nervous, or depressed? If so, the next time the urge hits, try telling yourself, "I need to find something else to do right away so that I don't feel bored, nervous, or depressed."

- The next time the urge to bite them comes, try some of this self-talk: "I really don't have to bite them", or "Biting them isn't really worth it".
- Try doing something else with your hands, for example, getting something to drink.
- Make a decision to stop. Tell someone else who may hold you accountable and ask how you're doing.
- Keep your nails trimmed and smooth so that you won't be tempted to bite them.
- Give yourself a treat, if you go one month without biting your nails. How about your favorite sundae or milk shake? How about a manicure?
- Try a bitter-tasting polish (or liquid) so your nails will taste badly if you bite them.
- If you still have problems, limit your biting to one nail.

Applying the Truth

1. God created your physical eyes to gather information. Your eyes, however, can receive both negative as well as positive input. It's important to protect yourself from the damage caused by negative influences. Teenagers must be careful, with all the pressures of society, to protect their mind and heart. Images teens allow into their minds affect their thought life as well as their attitudes.
2. Be quick to hear and slow to speak! It is more difficult to listen than it is to speak. When angry, you are more likely to speak first than be silent.
3. By keeping what comes into your eyes and ears as pure as possible; by using the G.I.G.O. principle to help you be more like Christ.

Chapter 10 Review Answers

Defining the Terms

Cirrhosis: a chronic disease of the liver that often results from a longstanding addiction to alcohol

Inhibitory effect: a result of alcohol that causes the blocking of the center of the brain that controls a person's degree of self-control and shyness

Alcoholism: an illness characterized by habitual, compulsive, long-term, and heavy drinking

Tolerance: a resistance in the body to something

Withdrawal: the physical disturbance that results when an individual does not consume a substance he/she is addicted to

MADD: Mothers Against Drunk Driving

Alcoholics Anonymous (AA): a support group specifically designed for alcoholics

Alateen: a group designed to help children of alcoholic parents

Al-Anon: a group designed to help the husbands, wives, and friends of alcoholics

Alexander Fleming: discovered the drug penicillin in London in 1928

Drugs: substances that alter the function of one or more body organs

Medicines: drugs that are meant to relieve pain, cure diseases, or prevent other illnesses

Drug abuse: a condition that occurs when a person uses an illegal drug or misuses a legal one

Prescription drugs: drugs that are sold only with a written order from a doctor

Nonprescription drugs: "over-the-counter" drugs that are medicines that can be sold without a doctor's written permission

FDA: The U.S. Food and Drug Administration tests drugs to make sure they are safe.

Side effects: any reactions to a drug other than the effect intended

Caffeine: a stimulant

Stimulants: drugs that speed up the body's nervous system

Addiction: a physical or mental need for a drug or other substance

Depressants: drugs that tend to slow down your body's nervous system

Narcotics: a form of depressant that induces sleep or decreases feeling

Morphine and codeine: highly addictive narcotics that are prescribed as painkillers

Heroin: an illegal drug that is a depressant and is extremely dangerous

PCP or angel dust (phencyclidine): an extremely dangerous hallucinogen

LSD (lysergic acid diethylamide): an extremely dangerous hallucinogen

Hallucinogen: a group of drugs that cause the brain to form unreal images

Inhalants: substances whose fumes are breathed in to give the user a high-like feeling, can cause permanent brain damage

Denial: refusing to acknowledge the existence of a problem

Nicotine: a colorless, oily, water-soluable, highly toxic and addictive, liquid alkaloid obtained from tobacco

Tar: a thick, dark, sticky liquid that is formed when tobacco burns

Carbon monoxide: a poisonous gas that is produced by car engines and burning tobacco

Emphysema: an irreversible lung disease that is primarily caused by smoking

Second-hand smoke (passive smoke): the smoke you breathe that comes from another person's smoking

Mainstream smoke: the smoke that is inhaled and then exhaled by the smoker

Sidestream smoke: the smoke that comes out of the end of a lit cigarette

Environmental smoke: the smoke that stays in the air where smokers have been smoking

Recalling the Facts

1. Show responsibility, gain more freedom; show more responsibility, gain more freedom. Freedom is something that a teenager earns, not demands.
2. • Increased freedom gives teens more time and exposure to learn about substances. Increased curiosity from asking questions such as, "What would it be like?"
   • More freedom gives teens a greater opportunity to discover and express their own individuality.
3. • Slurred speech
   • Inability to walk straight
   • Forgetfulness
   • Acting obnoxious
   • Endangering themselves or others
   • Assaulting someone
   • Embarrassing themselves
4. Advertiser's promote the pleasures and 'cool' image associated with the use of tobacco, alcohol, and other products that are dangerous to your health. You don't see a commercial of a person experiencing a hangover from drinking too much.
5. Coffee, tea and many soda pops are high in caffeine that is a stimulant. Caffeine increases the body's nervous system which can cause withdrawal symptoms. People who drink a lot of pop, tea, and coffee and then go without it, may experience headaches, weakness and a general sense of mental distraction from the body's strong craving. The more you drink a caffeinated beverage, the greater your body's demand for it will be.
6. • Causes irregular heartbeat
   • Increases hunger
   • Slows down the body's rate of development
   • Lowers body temperature
   • Impairs perception and response time
   • Damages the immune system
   • Hurts the reproductive system
   • Injures brain cells
   • Causes the user to view reality in a distorted way
7. Just one try of a drug can start a lifetime of addiction. Drugs today are more potent and dangerous than years ago. One try can end in death.
8. Possible answers may be:
   • Curiosity
   • Look cool
   • Peer pressure
   • Want to feel a "buzz"
   • Want to rebel against their parent's rules
   • Think they will quit when they get older
   • Feel indestructible ("I'll never get cancer. Other people smoke, and they're still living.")

Applying the Truth

1. To make it through today's culture you must have your own personal convictions (strong beliefs). You cannot rely only upon what your parents believe. You must have your own personal relationship with God and begin to make your own decisions based on the Scriptures about the issues that confront you.
2. • Avoid an argument with your parents (*Proverbs* 17:14);
   • Have lots of friends (*Proverbs* 18:24);
   • Earn money for a bike or a car (*Proverbs* 10:4);
   • Choose the best friends (*Proverbs* 22:24); and,
   • Choose the best girlfriend and wife (*Proverbs* 19:14; 31:10-31)
3. • Since God is love (*I John* 4:16), He wants you to experience His love so that you can show it to others.
   • Since one of the fruit of the Spirit is joy (*Galatians* 5:22) and, as David wrote to God, "In Your presence is fullness of joy" (*Psalm* 16:11), He wants you to feel His joy inside of your heart so that you can share it.
   • Since one of the fruit of the Spirit is peace (*Galatians* 5:22), Paul recommends when you are full of anxiety, "Let your requests be made known to God" (*Philippians* 4:6), so that you can know, "... the peace of God that surpasses all understanding will guard your hearts and minds through Christ Jesus" (*Philippians* 4:7).
   • Since Jesus has all supernatural power at His disposal (*Matthew* 28:17), He wants you to encounter some of His power so that you can help a hurting and dying world.

Chapter 11 Review Answers

Defining the Terms

Comprehension: understanding and remembering what you've read

Intellectual: mental; having to do with your mind

Regress: to go backward

Humility: realizing your own limitations

Hypocrites: "two-faced", giving the impression that you have certain beliefs, or feelings that you really don't have

Countenance: the expression of your face

Recalling the Facts

1. • Martin Luther, church reformer
   • John Calvin, church reformer
   • John Wycliffe, church reformer, Bible translator
   • Charles Finney, evangelist
   • John Wesley, founder of Methodism
2. • The next time you watch a movie, look at the credits and see what book the movie was taken from. Many—if not most—movies come from already-published books. Read the book upon which your favorite movie was based. Compare the book with the movie.
   • Tell yourself that you're going to spend just as much time reading as you do watching TV or movies.
   • Try not using any electronic entertainment for a day, a week, or more. See if you get better grades, develop more friendships, have fun learning something new, or get more good books read.
   • Find a friend who likes to read the same kind of books that you do.
   • Use a Bible translation that you really understand and like.
   • Help to put together a home environment that is favorable to reading.
3. Questions are good as long as they come from a heart that is simply seeking the truth. An attitude of pride, trying to be obnoxious, or trying to make someone be embarrassed or "look bad" are ways that questioning can be wrong. Check your motives and the timing of when to ask what question.
4. • Looking at them when they're talking to you;
   • Acknowledging what they've said to you by repeating it back to them, or saying "Yes, Mom";
   • Asking them to reconsider by giving them a good reason if you are struggling with what they've just asked you to do;
   • Saying, "Please" more often; and
   • Showing a grateful spirit toward all that they have done for you by saying "Thank you" more often.
5. One of the ways that you can show respect for your parents is in allowing them to "save face". As you mature, you're going to make some mistakes and so are your parents. Your parents have a lot of pressure on them to "be right" and "do right" most of the time. Because of this pressure, they usually won't appreciate it if you expose their mistakes in a direct or disrespectful way; some won't like it at all. But, as you get older, you're going to see legitimate problems in your parents. The fact is that everybody has weaknesses because we're all fallen and broken human beings in need of God.

Applying the Truth

1. Answers will vary.
2. • What was it like when you were a teen?
   • What jobs did you have when you were a teen?
   • Do you have any ideas of what kind of job(s) I could get?
   • I know that I'll be making my own decision, but what kind of career do you think that I might be good at?
   • What kind of relationship did you have with your Dad or Mom? Did you ever get into any struggles or arguments with them? If so, about what? How did you resolve them?
   • If you were to relive your teen years, what would you do the same? What would you do differently?
   • Did you ever struggle with your faith in God?

Chapter 12 Review Answers

Defining the Terms

Prayer: talking to God and listening to hear what God would say to you

Fear: concern or anxiety about something real or imagined

Influence: the power of a person or thing to persuade or take advantage of you

Destiny: a purpose that God has created for you

Recalling the Facts

1. What your parents, teachers, and pastors have taught you about God is likely to be the same way that you think about Him. If your parents are easy to talk to and very understand-

ing, you'll probably see God in that way, too. But, if your parents are distant or too busy for you, you might begin to think that God is the same way–even though He isn't.

2. • To help you to love God more (develop a closer relationship with Him).
   • To show you how to love people more (like Jesus loves them).
3. Keeping your prayer "hot-line" open to God all day. Talking to God, even briefly, throughout your day. Thanking Him as well as asking Him for guidance.
4. Many of them only take one step at a time. This is the way the characters in the Bible lived, too. Why doesn't God show you a complete picture of your life all at once? It's because He wants you to learn to live by faith; to trust Him to put together each piece of your Life Puzzle in His own time and in His own way. If you're not sure what your next step is in fulfilling your special purpose, then start asking Him, and He'll begin to let you know. God's more anxious for you to discover His unique plan for you than you are to discover it!

Applying the Truth

1. One of the subtle ways that the enemy will use to try to get you to compromise your standards is to get you involved with friends who have a negative influence upon you.
2. Satan loves to get you to sin. He knows that if he can make you feel so bad about yourself, you won't tell anyone and you will stay away from your loving Father. He will lie to you about yourself. He wants you to believe terrible things about how others and God feel about you. Don't believe him! You can expect opposition from Satan if you really want to make things right. He will lie to you about how bad you are and how disappointed God and others are in you. Don't listen to him! *James* 4:7. Humble yourself and go directly to God and those whom you have offended. As a result, you will grow in your spiritual maturity and feel like a brand new person!
3. All of these aspects that teens don't like about being a Christian make following Jesus challenging and sometimes difficult. Some teens decide that becoming a Christian is too hard and choose not to believe. Others may pretend to love and serve God on the outside while inside they really don't want to pay the price to serve God. Consequently, they know how to "act" spiritual, yet lack a true relationship with Him. If you don't want to be a Christian "pretender", then ask the Lord to help you to know and love Him so much that you become willing to accept the things that you don't like about Christianity. In doing this, you'll be counting the cost of being a true follower of Jesus.

   I think that the Lord is disappointed and sad when a person fakes having a relationship with Him. He desires a real relationship with each person and knows that really knowing Him is the way to true happiness.
4. • Through the Bible
   • In my heart
   • Through other people (parents)
   • Through the Holy Spirit
   • Through worship
   • In my conscience
   • In my dreams
   • Through my experiences